I HEALED MY SONS OF AUTISM & YOU CAN TOO:

THE 7 KEYS TO CLEARING YOUR CHILD OF ADHD & AUTISM NATURALLY

By Andrea Anderson

IHealedMySons.com

I Healed My Sons of Autism & You Can Too: The 7 Keys to Clearing Your Child of ADHD & Autism Naturally

By Andrea Anderson

Printed in the United States of America by Vervante.com

Edited by Ned Rozell and Lisa Alexander

Book Cover Design by Heidi Sutherlin, www.MyCreativePursuits.com

Edition ISBNs

Soft cover: 978-1-938579-60-8
Digital: 978-1-939795-14-4

Soft cover:
Library of Congress Control Number: 2013903774

1st Edition, March 2013

TABLE OF CONTENTS

AUTHOR'S NOTE   7

DEDICATION   9

FAMILY PICTURES   11

SECTION 1 - INTRODUCTION   15

- Introduction   17
- Why Did I Write this Book?   22
- Who Am I?   23
- What this Book is Not   25
- Who Stands to Gain the Most from Reading (and Following) the Key Steps in this Book?   26

SECTION 2 - A CLOSER LOOK AT ASDS   29

- What Life Looks Like With ASDs   31
- What Can a Life Cleared of Autism and other ASDs Look Like?   32
- A Life Without ASDs is Not Perfect   34
- What You Learn in This Book Can Be Applied to Help Heal ANY Area of Your Life   34
- What I've Noticed   35
- Everyone Else is Doing It   37
- Empty Cup Theory   38
- Why Does this Seem to Happen to Only Some Adults and Children but Not Everyone?   40
- The BEST news: This condition is Improvable and Potentially Reversible!   41

SECTION 3 - THE MOM MINDSET I ACQUIRED TO HELP   43
HEAL MY SONS OF AUTISM

- The Mom Mindset I Acquired to Help Heal My Sons of Autism   45
- HELP Heal Mindset   48
- H- Honor Your Feelings   49
- E- Everything Happens for a Reason   52
- L- Learn from Your Children   56
- P- Prioritize YOU   61
- Life Before When I Only Focused on My Sons   62
- The Result of Loosening the Reigns of the Supermom Mindset   64
- Summary of The HELP Heal Mindset   65
- The 7 RESTORE Keys   66

RESTORE KEY R - REALITY REWRITTEN   69

- Create a New Story   71
- Universal Law   73
- How Does this Apply to My Family and Our Situation?   74

RESTORE KEY E - EAT NATURAL REAL FOODS   79

- What Foods Qualify as Real and Natural   81
- What Foods are Better for You to Eat?   83
- Why is Natural Food Better for You?   86
- If You Put Junk In, You'll Get Junk Out   88
- Keep Your Food Simple   88
- Foods that Can Aggravate ADHD and All ASDs   90
- Food Sensitivity   91
- Go Slow with Diet Changes   93
- One More Food to Think About   93

RESTORE KEY S - SIMPLE DAILY BODY CLEANSE   97

- Why Would You and Your Family Want to Clean Toxins Out of Your Body?   99
- Clean the Body Out: Get Movin'   101
- Clean the Body Out: Drink Lots of Water   104
- Clean the Body Out: It's Time to Poop!   105
- Clean the Body Out: Use Supplements & Food   106
- Another Cleansing Approach   107

RESTORE KEY T - THRIVE IN NATURAL BALANCED ENVIRONMENTS ... 109

- Our New Home ... 111
- Your Family Doctor ... 114
- Back to the Basics ... 115
- EMFs ... 118
- Time at School ... 119
- How Does Your House Make You Feel? ... 122
- What's Displayed in Your Home? ... 122

RESTORE KEY O - "OM", LISTEN TO YOUR INTUITION ... 125

- Boden's Six-Month Doctor's Visit ... 127
- What Exactly Is Intuition? ... 129
- How to Hear Your Intuition ... 132
- Additional Ways to Hear Your Intuition ... 133

RESTORE KEY R - RESPECT & APPRECIATE YOURSELF ... 137

- Why Is It Important to Respect and Appreciate Yourself? ... 139
- My Own Story ... 144
- Feeling Good Enough ... 146
- Respecting and Loving Myself Helped Heal My Sons ... 149
- How to Start the Process of LOVING YOU ... 151
- Self Love Exercises ... 152
  - 5 Minutes of Gratitude ... 152
  - Mirror ... 152
  - Watch What You Say ... 153
  - Speak Up for What You Want ... 155
  - Visualize ... 157
  - Make Peace with Limiting Thoughts ... 158
  - Forgiveness ... 158
  - Welcome Support ... 159
- Negative Self Thoughts Fill Up Your Cup ... 159

RESTORE KEY E - ESTABLISH BALANCE IN KEY AREAS OF LIFE   161

- What's the Purpose of Establishing Balance in Key Areas of Your Life?   163
- Health   165
- Career   165
- Relationship   166
- Spirituality   169
- My Spiritual Practice   169
- Movement   170
- Finances   171
- Fun   171
- Contribution   173
- Key Areas of Life- Summary   174

WRAP UP!   175

DON'T DO THIS ALONE   177

CONTINUE TO INVEST IN YOUR FAMILY'S WELL-BEING   178

THANK YOU TO MY FAMILY   178

MORE GRATITUDE   179

COACHES   182

COACHES FROM AFAR   183

DOCTORS   184

ABOUT THE AUTHOR   187

Author's note

The information contained in this book stems from my personal experiences, and has been related as I remember it. The stories I share are intended to better help you relate to the information.

In the case of my sons, my oldest son Forrest was diagnosed with PDD tendencies one year after we had already been following a few of the RESTORE Keys outlined in this book. Prior to following some of these key steps, he was showing signs of being further on the spectrum. The day I brought Forrest to a psychologist to be "analyzed," I sat in the doctor's office and filled out a behavior questionnaire. As I filled out the questionnaire, I looked up at the doctor and said, "Wow, if I had taken this questionnaire a few months ago, I would be answering VERY differently then I am now. I would have been checking off always and often for many of the questions about poor behavior." Instead I was checking off, occasionally.

My point: Forrest's label would have been even further along on the spectrum had we not already been helping him in a holistic manner.

My youngest son Boden wasn't officially diagnosed, but I knew in my heart what he had. At 7 ½ months old, when he lost all motor coordination, starting shaking his head and rolling his eyeballs to the back of his head, and would stare off into space, even after I called his name over 40 times, I knew something was wrong. Boden showed practically all of the symptoms described in every article I read on autism.

I didn't want to wait to hear from a specialist what my son had. I wasn't afraid to hear it, because I already knew. And, I thought, what good does a label do? I preferred to expend my energy on finding ways to help Boden and Forrest move past their symptoms and heal.

And, that is exactly what I did. They are both label-free and autism-free! This book and the information contained in it comes from my experiences, as well as my heart.

DEDICATION

This book is dedicated to all families looking to make life better and easier for their child.

FAMILY PICTURES

Forrest & Boden first day of school 2012

I set the camera timer and tried to take some family photos... Here's what ensued:

Photo One- Boden singing and Forrest trying to look like Justin Bieber.

Photo Two- Forrest getting ready to see how far he could throw a rock.

Photo Three- Boden deciding to be silly!

Ok, so who said taking self timed family photos was easy?

As you can see, my sons may be healed of autism, but they are unapologetically boys through and through! They goof around and yes, they don't always cooperate, but who does?

FYI the photo on the cover of this book is of my sons. I snapped the photo while on vacation on Assateague Island in Maryland. My sons were about 4 & 7 years old and were in the middle of trying to tickle each other when I decided to take a few pictures.

SECTION 1

INTRODUCTION

INTRODUCTION

We're in Arlington National Cemetery in Washington D.C. It's a bright sunny day. We're attending a funeral for my step grandmother, a beautiful woman who lived a long wonderful life, with many happy adventures along the way. The event is less about sadness and more about respect and appreciation; love lingers in the air.

My sons are listening attentively as a Marine is standing by my step grandmother's vase of ashes, relaying an account of her beautiful blessed life. I'm taking in the moment, the sun is shining bright, the breeze is gently blowing my hair against my cheeks. Little tears form in the corners of my eyes as I recall my step grandmother and the wonderful woman she was. As I'm taking this in, my sons and husband are glancing around at the people in attendance, the thousands of white tombstones. My sons are both standing still, like statues. I feel my youngest son Boden's hand in mine. I feel grateful. I feel grateful to be here. I feel grateful for my family, I feel grateful for this moment. Some of the people in attendance at this funeral have heard my sons had autism spectrum disorders (ASDs), but no one really knows they're completely healed. In this moment I have forgotten this splendid fact, instead, in this moment, I just feel at peace. It feels good to have my kids listening, interested, calm and at peace with themselves.

Later that same day we attend an after-funeral reception. My sons sit calmly and comfortably, eating some hors d'oeuvres and chatting with their grandparents.

That same evening we complete our day with a dinner out with several people who were at the funeral. As everyone chats at the restaurant, I talk with a family member who comments on how good my sons are.

"Wow," she says. "Your mother told me about the boys, you would never have known they had anything — they sat so well, they're so polite."

That's when it hit me — people don't expect someone to heal from autism. They think, okay, maybe they can make things a little better for them. But complete healing, it just can't happen. Right?

At that moment, I receive my epiphany as to what helped me to heal my sons. It was my expectation that they would heal. I would not listen to outside thoughts and ideas. I was clear what I wanted — complete healing — and that's what was happening. Absolutely, definitely happening. How cool is that? My sons defy expectations — they are healed!

Fast forward to a school language assembly for my sons. My oldest son

Forrest is 10 and my youngest son Boden is 7. Both of them are performing on stage with their class. They are learning Spanish and German in school and this performance shares with parents and family members some of their newfound language skills. This is Boden's first time up on the "big" stage, while Forrest has a few years of similar experiences. They sing, dance, recite poems and act silly, all while speaking only Spanish and then only German.

The performances are over. Forrest knew all of his lines and said them comfortably and clearly. Boden sang and easily danced the proper dance steps without missing a beat.

My heart fills with happiness; it's beautiful and wonderful that both of my sons are doing so well. They are learning, growing and evolving into the beautiful souls that were always inside of them, just previously hidden to themselves and the world because of other things affecting their bodies physically and mentally. My sons are cleared now. They are healthy and strong and learning just like any other child learns. Yes, I am very appreciative of this!

Life wasn't always this easy, nor did it always feel so wonderful.

My past looked like this:

Both of my sons were born typical or normal, but were affected by toxins-pesticides, insecticides, unfiltered tap water, and vaccinations. As a result, they ended up being on the autism spectrum. My youngest son, Boden had been developing nicely and after his 6.5-month vaccinations, lost all of his motor coordination and began to stare into space and seem distant. He also began to shake his head rapidly and roll his eyeballs to the back of his head. This behavior had me wanting to throw up every time I saw it!

After much testing, doctors said he was "okay" and to "keep an eye on it."

I knew all wasn't okay and I took matters into my own hands. I read, researched and uncovered what I sensed the problem was — all signs pointed to autism.

In the meanwhile, my husband and I had been contending with our older son who, over the past four years of his life, shared with us behaviors we were not always able to manage. Forrest experienced atypical mood swings. He'd go from being happy and calm to hitting and aggressive in a moment. Nobody was ever quite sure what was affecting him. Back then I blamed myself and my husband's parenting skills. Forrest was also very hyper, and would very often focus on one thing for only minutes at a time. He wasn't a child who played for hours with a toy, he played with something very briefly and then moved on.

With Forrest, play dates very often ended up with us leaving abruptly because Forrest hurt this playmate. We'd leave in a hurry, with me crying. Forrest was clueless as to what was going on. How I wished my child could be like everyone else's child — kind, gentle and well-behaved. I felt sorry for myself.

As time progressed, it became more apparent that Boden (our youngest son) was "off." He didn't walk until he was almost two-and-a-half. This was with the help of a physical therapist and an intervention team the state provided to us because he qualified. He didn't seem to play with toys or other children. He too entered into major-temper-tantrum-aggressive mode over time.

There were so many times when my husband and I just didn't know what to do. We felt like we didn't know how to control our own children at times and it was really affecting our relationship. We would argue over what we perceived to be the best parenting approach. We blamed each other for what we saw going wrong with our kids.

We were confused, scared, worn out and defeated. How the hell can we help this get better? At times we lost hope and thought maybe it couldn't get better than this.

Lucky for me, a voice inside me told me otherwise. Yes, Andrea it can get better. You all deserve better, keep going, it's all okay.

With this thought, I continued to persevere. We began seeing a DAN — Defeat Autism Now — doctor. She practices biogenetics — healing the core of the problem, not just the symptoms. Eventually we added other holistic doctors and experts to the mix.

And so, my healing journey began.

This endeavor took my family and I down a path that was anything but regular. We had to step off the mainstream and open up to doing many, many things differently. It was stepping away from what everyone else was doing, re-examining what was best for us and pursuing a new course of living, a more natural way of living, that made a difference. We had to resist, even reject what our friends, family, commercials, TV and society told us was important.

A funny thing happened. When we stopped conforming and did things more naturally, this is where true healing occurred.

The ride to restoring my children from autism spectrum disorders wasn't easy and yet, it became the most pivotal event in my life.

As a mom and a woman, I love more because of it. I appreciate more because of it. I'm more open and confident because of it. I'm more real because of it. My family and I have a higher quality of life because of it.

This might sound extreme, and you might even be saying to yourself, great for you, but that's not my reality. I understand, this wasn't always my reality, but it is now. I took one step at a time, was willing to learn and grow, I looked at my kids and myself, and I kept believing it was possible. Eventually, it was.

I want you to know this can be for you too. Healing is possible.

WHY DID I WRITE THIS BOOK?

I wrote this book because **I've healed my sons and I want to help others do the same.**

I want to show others that it is possible to restore your child from autism spectrum disorders. It doesn't have to be a life sentence. You have options.

I want everyone to have the same wonderful level of healing I've experienced with my sons.

So many families are struggling, looking for answers, feeling unsure, tired, confused, defeated. It's time to change that. It's time for parents to find answers and peace of mind. It's time for children to heal. I want people to know it's completely possible to have a life that feels easier, to have happiness and harmony back in your life. It's also possible to have children who are relaxed and thriving — making friends, doing well in school, more at peace with themselves.

It's time to acknowledge this — you and your family deserve a great life!! We all deserve this. Life is meant to be easy. If you've resolved to feeling life is about struggling (I understand, I've been there with this same thinking) keep reading. Hopefully through my example you will glean some important ideas to help your child's condition greatly improve.

Who am I?

I'm a mother who really cares about her sons and who has really learned to care about herself, the second half of this being the most difficult.

Back in the day, when the s*%t started to hit the fan, that is, when I first learned that my sons had ASDs, I did everything in my power to help them. I read books, researched, attended conferences, saw holistic doctors, and changed our way of living and eating habits.

I also returned to school, the Institute for Integrative Nutrition in NYC. This school was a game changer for me. I went to the school not necessarily to heal my sons, but to heal me. I was so worn out from helping my kids heal — I thought about it all day, applied everything I came to know, dreamt about it. Every waking hour was dedicated to them. My body was crying out for help and attention. When I came across the information for the school, something in me said yes. I knew what I would learn there would help my sons, but I sensed and hoped what I would learn there would help me. There was this feeling and additional motivation within me to take whatever I learned there and make it a career. Somehow I knew I wanted to help others heal.

That's exactly what happened.

Going back to school helped me begin the journey of healing myself, which brought further healing to my sons — big time!

Through years of trying different techniques- for myself and my sons and my family overall- (thank you, by the way Shane - my husband, for going along for the ride and trying all these different approaches to healing), I learned what really works and makes a difference in restoring children from ASDs.

As I started seeing marked differences in my sons, I began a coaching and speaking practice. I felt that between my school and personal experience I could comfortably guide people to heal their bodies through nutrition.

I initially helped people lose weight, heal digestive concerns, learn to love themselves and live confidently, through nutrition and other holistic means.

I enjoyed this, but something was still missing. Then I realized what was under my nose all along. I learned how to restore my sons' bodies from ASDs. This, my friend, is a gift I need to share in the world. I've lived and breathed this journey day in and day out. I've come to see what works and what doesn't. It's been a long journey and now, I can help others make the journey — maybe even make the trip more easily than I did!

I'm now speaking and coaching others on this stuff. It feels like this is what I'm meant to be doing right now — sharing my knowledge and experience to help make life better for anyone who's interested.

WHAT THIS BOOK IS NOT

I wrote this book from a place of honesty, from my heart. What I recall from what I've experienced and learned is exactly what I wrote on these pages. I understand this book is not for everybody — it might feel too extreme or different for some. That's okay. I want you to know regardless of where you stand, you can trust me, and if this approach feels right, I can help you.

I'm not promising I can fix everything for you. You're not going to read this book and everything will magically be better. It will take some time and effort, and even then, some of you will find what I offer works for you, while other people will remain stuck. This is the way it is. No promises. I simply am letting you know, I've done it, and it is possible you can too.

I'm not trying to convince you in this book. I'm simply sharing my insights, experience, and knowledge organized in a way to help you follow the steps for yourself and your family, if you choose.

If you question my ideas, that's fine. It's healthy to question things. Follow what I say if you sense it's the right thing for you and your family. If you question my ideas and they feel off — you're welcome to return this book and collect your money back.

WHO STANDS TO GAIN THE MOST FROM READING (AND FOLLOWING) THE KEY STEPS IN THIS BOOK?

There are some people this book (and it's ideas) just won't be able to help. It's a mindset thing. Those with certain mindsets will reach success with my approach to clearing ADHD and autism, while other mindsets will not. Check in with yourself to see if you're a good fit for my approach, if you are, you stand a greater chance of benefiting from the information I share.

You're a great match- and stand to make more progress with clearing your child of their ASD if:

- You're open minded
- You're ready to move past complaining and blaming and take responsibility for your life and your child's
- You've tried some holistic approaches to living- yoga, you shop at a health food store, or you're really immersed in it- full on natural living for you- or you haven't gotten into holistic living but you're

open to it, it really appeals to you (this was me for sometime- open to it, but not living it!)

- Open and willing to go beyond what your doctor recommends
- Willing to try a new approach even before statistics and studies have proven its efficacy (I think of this as being on the leading edge of progress!)
- Motivated, like to get things done
- You don't wait for people to fix things for you; you jump in and take care of business!
- You're willing to do what it takes to help your child – even if it means turning your attention to yourself and seeing how you can improve as a mom AND you're willing to do the self work to grow
- You're willing and ready to improve your lifestyle
- You're ready for something better and bigger for your child and your family
- You have the full on intention to pave the way for a much easier better life for your child and want the same for yourself too!

If the above statements describe you, lets move on, you're definitely in a position to make excellent progress with clearing your child's ADHD or autism.

If you're feeling as though you may not be a good fit for this approach, that's ok. You have two choices: either return the book and collect your money back, or continue reading and see if perhaps you can glean a tip or two along the way, something that may lead to some level of improvement for your child. Your choice. Good luck.

I HEALED MY SONS OF AUTISM AND YOU CAN TOO:

SECTION 2

A Closer Look at ASDs

What Life Looks Like with ASDs

ASDs very often rule families' lives. Your life doesn't feel like your life, it feels like it belongs to the ASD. People don't make choices based on what they would really like to be doing, they make choices based on what they think would be best for their child with the ASD or what would be easiest. Behaviors like temper tantrums cause people to not want to leave the house, for fear they won't be able to control their child. The inability of the child to sit still causes parents to skip going out to dinner or anywhere their child might be expected to sit quietly for some time. Simple routines like going to the grocery store can take on a new dimension, not necessarily going as easy as one might want. (I remember this all too well!)

When my oldest son was about 3 years old, we had just moved to a new town. I remember wanting to meet people, but not wanting to go out very often because it was easier to stay at home than deal with the humiliation

of temper tantrums and aggressive behavior that would surface sporadical-
ly. I spent many, many days in my yard and in my home. I had fun with my
children (mostly), I just felt very limited in what I could do with them.

ASDs can create lots of self-doubt, worry and fear. Take my example, I
allowed myself to become fearful of leaving the house with my children. I
was afraid that Forrest would behave in a way that would have me judged
poorly and I wouldn't be able to calm him down. I was *fearful*. Not only
was I fearful, I was doubtful of my skills. I had seen many times before that
I couldn't completely handle my son. What made me think some magic
would arise to help me handle the situation any differently? Even with
guidance from a counselor, I still found Forrest's behavior to be inconsis-
tent and not always consolable. When ASDs lead your life, as they so often
do, sadness, struggle, fear and doubt are the emotions that permeate the
entire family. No one in the family, the children nor the parents feel completely in control — life is consumed by the ASD.

What Can a Life Cleared of Autism and Other ASDs Look Like?

Life feels freer and more comfortable. You make decisions where to go out
to eat based on what food you're in the mood for – not because they have
the most understanding wait staff that doesn't judge you when your child
acts up.

You travel to different states via plane. Yes, that's right, by plane. Sitting for
long periods of time talking, laughing, reading and yes, sitting quietly (or
at least fairly quietly.)

Your children go to school, learn right along side all of the other children and evolve academically, emotionally and socially in a similar fashion to all the other children in their class.

As a parent you feel confident and empowered. You have the skills and knowledge and awareness of great resources to help your children every step of the way. You finally feel like you know what you're doing. You feel in control of your life.

You also feel really good about yourself. Having watched your children go from a more imbalanced state of living to thriving is one of the most amazing feelings in the world. I cry just thinking about it!

When symptoms of an ASD are cleared, other areas of your life begin to fall into place. Communication in the family can go from yelling to talking. Children and families now have harmony restored to their lives and their homes. Siblings have the opportunity to get to know each other better. They can begin to see the good in each other. What previously was a cold or aggressive relationship now opens up. Siblings find they have common interests, or, just enjoy playing and spending time together.

Parents begin to spend more time together, because they can. They're no longer living in crisis mode, now they can turn their attention to their long forgotten partner. If chosen, relationships can improve and love can flourish again.

When autism and other ASDs are improved- families begin to HEAL.

A Life Without ASDs is Not Perfect

To be clear, when your child clears from autism or any ASD, life is still not picture perfect. Life will never be perfect. You will have challenges and disappointments along the way to be sure. This is the evolution of life, it's what helps us all to continue to grow. Children and their family members will still argue, siblings might not always happily get along. That's okay. Even as I was finishing this book, one of my sons had some old behaviors we thought he was past, resurface. I thought to myself, holy heck, here I am writing this book on healing our kids and what's happening to mine. As it turns out, he's completely back on track now, just had to make some minor adjustments, but, the point is, life never moves perfectly smooth in one direction.

The truth is, once your kids' symptoms improve, life begins to feel easier. Much easier. The other challenges that surface can be handled with more care and understanding because you have the energy and focus to give to the concern, you also have the wisdom and resources to tap into to resolve other life problems with more ease and grace.

What You Learn in this Book Can Be Applied to Help Heal ANY Area of Your Life

Might sound crazy but it's true! Any area of your life can benefit if you apply the HELP Heal Mindset and the 7 RESTORE Keys.

These RESTORE Keys combined with the HELP Heal Mindset are really just a healthy approach to living. As with any healthy approach to living, if applied to other areas of your life, will help you to create more balance and positivity in that area.

WHAT I'VE NOTICED

I've noticed that the world is changing. Technology is everywhere. It's unusual for someone to not have a cell phone or computer. Reaching out to someone to have a quick conversation or collect a quick answer to a question is super easy and convenient. Yes, technology is fantastic. For those of you reading this on your Kindle or computer, obviously this way of connecting with you wouldn't be possible if it weren't for the advancement of technology. My business continues to grow and prosper as a result of the Internet and technology. I love and appreciate technology, it's wonderful. It's added a tremendous amount of convenience to our lives.

Life, when lived at it's best, is all about experiencing things in balance. When a tipping point occurs, like when we're more about technology and less about living in a way that's natural, connected to nature and what's naturally best for us, we start to see the effects.

Technology has sped us up as a human race. People have come to expect things quickly. Messages come quickly via cell phones, Internet, any show you could possibly dream of is out there quickly available to watch, any bit of information you would like to research is easily and quickly at your fingertips.

The same goes for our food. Our food has sped up. People want quick and easy. With that notion in mind, companies have designed products that can be made in a jiffy. Microwaves are in some cases used more than a stove. It's all about convenience baby!! If it ain't quick, many people won't even purchase it or try it! I get it, time is important, it's a hot commodity and when we gain more of it for ourselves, life feels easier and nicer.

Large and small companies have noticed this trend and have helped us along with feeding into this "fast" craze. In order to create products that can be made quickly and still taste good, they began creating processed foods. These foods were a novelty initially. Instant oatmeal, macaroni and cheese, chocolate milk. The concern with all this instant food was that they were not whole foods or real foods, they were processed foods. Foods that now had artificial flavors, colors and other unnatural additives blended in. At first, because people were still essentially eating lots of natural, real foods, like fruits and veggies and clean protein, adding in a sprinkling of processed foods didn't have a huge impact. Over time, this changed.

Now when you enter into a grocery store you'll notice the majority of what's being sold is processed foods full of unnatural additives.

Try putting this to the test. Walk down any center isle in the grocery store and pick up a random box of something and read the ingredients. I'll venture to guess perhaps 95% of what you pick up will have some type of chemical, artificial additive or preservative.

The majority of the food created now is no longer natural.

What's the big deal with eating foods with additives and preservatives?

EVERYONE ELSE IS DOING IT

What's this all mean? What's the big deal with eating foods with additives and preservatives anyway, everyone else is doing it, the products taste good and after-all, they're the easiest and cheapest to buy and make.

Yes, everybody else is eating this stuff, because it is so prevalent, heavily advertised and the most convenient to locate, purchase and prepare.

Here's the thing, and I'm sure you've heard this statement before, just because everybody else is doing it, doesn't make it right. It just makes it what everybody else is doing.

If you look closer at what everyone else is doing, you'll also find a lot of unhappy, grouchy parents, children with behavior concerns, disconnected family relationships and unhealthy bodies.

Yes, this too is something that most other people have, but is this something you want to continue to recreate for yourself?

If the answer is no, then you'll want to begin to stop doing what everyone else is doing. You'll want to *think differently* and learn how to see what's true and best for you and your family, not just follow the crowd.

I had my own wake-up call when I first learned my sons were on the autism spectrum. We as a family ate packaged processed foods, mac and cheese, processed cheese dip, packaged instant rice dishes, etc. Believe, me, we were in the mix with everyone else. What finally separated us from the rest of the pack, so-to-speak, was taking a leap of faith and doing things differently, in this case, eating differently. It became clear, if I wanted to heal my sons, it meant I needed to eat differently, to eat better and to live differently. Not easy at first, but enormously gratifying once I got into the swing of things. By the way, when I say gratifying, I mean as gratifying as saying goodbye to autism all together. It can get that good, really!!!!

The point I'm trying to make here: it may be easy, tasty and comfortable to eat processed, artificially enriched foods, but in the long run it does not serve you or your family's health and emotional well-being.

Why does this happen? Why are people's bodies affected by these less natural foods?

Allow me to answer that with what I've come to understand as a Truth. I refer to this as the Empty Cup Theory.

EMPTY CUP THEORY

We humans typically start our existence in this life with clean bodies. Think of your body as an empty cup. Over time, you can be inadvertently exposed to toxins. Each time you or your child is exposed to toxins, your cup fills up just a little. Over time, your child is exposed to chemicals from an array of sources. These sources are usually simple unobtrusive sources that most people don't even consider toxic, but with consistent exposure to them, your child's cup will fill.

Sources like: processed foods with unnatural food chemicals, pesticides on your lawn. Your child breathes this in, and his cup fills up a little more.

Your neighbor spreads insecticide around their house to keep the ants out. Your child breathes this in and her cup fills up yet a little more. You and your husband paint several rooms inside your house using unassuming regular paint. Their cup is filling up. You clean the house using chlorine or ammonia based cleaners, and you do this regularly. You guessed it, your child's cup is filling up! You bring your child to the doctors to get their regularly scheduled immunizations. His cup is really full now. You take a family vacation, traveling through the airport, going through the metal detector and body scan. The cup is now extremely full. All of these seemingly regular unobtrusive activities can all contribute to filling up your child's cup. And yours too! (See *What's Toxic and What's Not* by Dr Gary Ginsberg & Brian Toal for additional info.)

Most people haven't thought to question the sources of these toxins. Because the FDA or some other panel of "experts" has condoned some of them, they must be okay. Here's the thing, if just one of these products was consumed, inhaled or used in some way for a short while, without all the other products being used, then your body could more easily process it, excrete it and release it from your system. When your system is burdened with the task of excreting several unnatural substances— simultaneously and continuously, over and over (because you continue to eat and use these products) then your system becomes over taxed. It maxes out, and your body isn't able to get it all out. Your cup fills up and continues to fill up until it's so full it spills over.

This filling up translates into something breaking. Your body, or your child's body begins to stop functioning in the natural wonderful way it's meant to function. Illnesses can kick in. Children or adults end up with food allergies, unstable emotions. Neurological impairment occurs. Any organ can be affected. This is when autism, ADHD, ADD creeps in and makes itself known.

Your child who was previously developing well, begins to have physical setbacks. He or she has violent temper tantrums, displays aggressive behavior, shows difficulty listening, is impulsive and lacks patience or focus.

These are all signs that your child's cup is full and has now spilled over.

Why Does this Seem to Happen to Only Some Adults and Children but Not Everyone?

The operative word here is "seem." Anyone who's consistently eating, drinking and inhaling unnatural foods and substances is being affected. Some people will end up on the spectrum while others will end up with food allergies, eczema, depression, or act moody and feel angry a lot. Others will just plain get sick with illnesses that have them traveling to hospitals and doctor after doctor.

All of this is simply a case of needing to empty their cups, clean up their bodies — clear the toxins out — and replace what hasn't helped them with what does.

Some people have more difficulty removing toxins from their body.

It's true, some people have more difficulty than others removing toxins from their body.

Why? Holistic doctors who practice biogenetics (DAN doctors- Defeat Autisim Now) believe that some children and adults have a genetic pre-disposition that makes it more difficult to remove metals and other toxins from their body. When these individuals take in unnatural/ toxic substances, their body isn't able to fully chelate, to naturally detox the substances out. As a result, their cup fills up at a faster rate than someone whose body can naturally and more easily chelate or remove these substances.

THE BEST NEWS: THIS CONDITION IS *IMPROVABLE* AND POTENTIALLY *REVERSIBLE*!

Yes, this condition is improvable for sure, and when sought after with complete belief, reversible.

Living in sync with nature is one of the big answers. This means living more naturally. By the way, living naturally doesn't mean you have to live in a tent out in the woods and only eat berries and nuts. You can still live your beautiful life, with the creature comforts that you've grown accustom to. Now you'll just want to take your life to the next level.

How?

The HELP Heal Mindset, combined with the 7 RESTORE Keys I share in this book, will set the stage for you and your family to empty your child's cup and potentially clear their ASD.

After lots of reflecting, I have organized the foundational pieces of what I did, my "how to" steps of healing my sons, into two areas. The HELP Heal

Mindset and the 7 RESTORE Keys. Each of these areas was instrumental in clearing my sons of ASDs, and continue on many levels to keep us all healthy and balanced.

I share with you now from my heart what I have found to be hugely important for us on our healing journey. I hope it proves to be as helpful to you too.

SECTION 3

THE MOM MINDSET I ACQUIRED TO HELP HEAL MY SONS OF AUTISM

The Mom Mindset I Acquired to Help Heal My Sons of Autism

For a very, very long time, I functioned from a place of the Supermom Mindset. I tried to do everything in my power to help my kids be happy and live a comfortable life. I drove them from activity to activity, set up play-dates, found the best-fit schools for them, volunteered at school whenever possible, cooked, baked and planned ahead for all outings by bringing snacks, drinks and activities to keep everyone content. I stayed up until midnight making nice lunches, filling out school forms, and getting organized for each day. My life was all about my kids.

Once it came to my attention that my kids were on the spectrum, I then somehow put it into high gear (as if I wasn't doing this already) and began to do *even more* for my kids. My to do list included visiting holistic doctors, administering holistic therapies and physical therapies, reading, researching, making special food to bring everywhere (once I learned my kids had allergies.) I was going 180 miles an hour; my goal was to be a good mom and do what was best for my kids. Or so I thought.

I had every symptom of the **Supermom Mindset:**

- Thinks of her kids first
- Rarely thinks of herself, feels guilty if she does
- Spends little to zero time with her husband, or friends
- Tries to fix everything
- Overcommits because she tries to make everyone happy
- Has a difficult time saying no
- Gets angry at herself if she yells at her child

So many women have this mindset. As a matter of fact, it's the norm. If this is you, don't feel bad. Society has promoted this mindset. For hundreds of years women were taught to dutifully follow the "good woman or good wife mindset" or the Supermom Mindset.

Think back to the Pilgrims, the first English settlers in the U.S. They weren't exactly a fun bunch of high-spirited do-for-yourself-draw-the-line-say-no-and-let-go-of-guilt sort of women. They were the opposite. They worked hard and committed themselves to do what they thought of as the noble thing: thinking of their family first. They *only* thought of their family and rarely themselves.

From a positive standpoint, this mindset has allowed you to help your child to a large degree. It's gotten you this far. It's helped to keep you motivated, disciplined, and on track with doing so much that's already made an enormous difference in your child's life. But if you're interested in taking the steps to enhance their progress, you'll want to get intimately familiar with a new mindset, one that helps you to do more for your child and make greater progress than what you've reached so far.

Even though the Supermom Mindset has been helpful, it's also held you back in some ways. Looking more closely at the Supermom Mindset, you'll notice it will have you running around in circles, filling your schedule with a million to-dos for the family. You can feel like you have little to no time to be with friends let alone be with your husband or yourself. Life feels hectic and overwhelming at times. You find yourself crying at times because you feel like your family doesn't fully respect you or think of your needs and concerns — it feels like everyone takes you for granted.

Because it's a rarity that you spend time with your spouse, your relationship suffers — how can something grow if you don't take care of it?!

Since you're so busy taking care of everyone else, especially your kids, your health starts to wane, if you're not taking care of yourself, your health can remain strong for only so long before it catches up with you.

You gain weight. Instead of speaking up for yourself and telling your family and others how you really feel and what you really want, you try to make everyone else happy. Without even realizing it, you then end up reaching for a bag of chips, cookies, crackers whatever, to appease this sad, unheard, ignored side of you. Food is turned to for comfort. But the comfort is short-lived and guilt kicks in. You then berate yourself for eating too much! This guilt only compounds your craving for specific foods.

Does any of this sound familiar? Having a Supermom Mindset can lead to any and all of these symptoms. (Take it from me, I LIVED ALL OF THEM!!)

While being a supermom seems wonderful on the outside, on the inside, when you peel the layers away, you see just how unhealthy it can be. Nobody is truly served as well as they could be when you follow the Supermom Mindset, it only appears that way at first glance. To the outside world you look like a terrific mom, but at home, alone with your family, you feel like crap!

When it comes to healing your child, the Supermom Mindset will only take you so far. **If you're interested in clearing your child of their ASD and consequently improving the quality of your life as well, you'll want to pay close attention to the HELP Heal Mindset.** It's the mindset I had to step into in order to make things really happen.

HELP HEAL MINDSET

What is the H.E.L.P. Heal Mindset — it's a way of thinking that allows you to upgrade your child's quality of life. **It's an integral component of clearing your child of ADHD or autism, or whatever ASD they may have.**

You'll want to pay attention to this, because the HELP Heal Mindset makes all the difference in the level of healing you achieve regardless of the approach you decide to follow. I want to place emphasis on this point: If you follow the 7 RESTORE Keys I share in this book or you follow a specific doctor's approach or an approach you researched on your own, you will find if you integrate this mindset into whatever approach you choose to implement, you will get farther, much farther. This HELP Heal Mindset is integral to clearing your child of ASDs. Integral! I just can't say that enough.

Acquiring the HELP Heal Mindset was pivotal in healing my sons!

The word **HELP**, in the **HELP Heal Mindset**- is an acronym –

> **H- Honor your feelings**
> **E- Everything happens for a reason**
> **L- Learn from your children**
> **P- Prioritize YOU, heal yourself too!**

H- Honor Your Feelings

I once thought I should to be happy all the time. I thought it wasn't okay to get angry and yell. A good mother doesn't yell at her kids, she seeks to understand them, hear them and even if they're not listening to her and really acting off the wall, she's suppose to remain calm and always, always act kind.

Wow, that's a lot to strive for- always, always be calm, kind, NEVER get angry or yell! (And, somehow, this is what I previously strived for!) Nobody in her right mind is always anything! We're human, we are happy and angry, we are calm and excited, we are sad and we are joyful. For every feeling we have there is its opposite. The opposite of happy is angry. When we ignore an opposite emotion, we are doing ourselves a disservice. We aren't honoring what we really feel. We're suppressing something. It might seem like the logical "better" thing to do, suppress anger. Why not, after all, anger is bad, right? But anger is real; it's a part of who you are, a part of who we all are. When anger (or any emotion) is ignored, something huge happens — it eventually surfaces, and when it does *watch out!* It can show up at inopportune times over something little, like when somebody spills something or your spouse says the wrong thing. This is what Debbie Ford, author of *The Dark Side of the Light Chasers*, refers to as the beach ball syndrome. It's the idea you can only hold a beach ball under water for so long before it shoots up into the air. Translation: if you feel anger and don't express it, that anger builds up inside of you. Eventually that anger will burst out, make itself known, and when it does you'll find yourself yelling, not sure what happened and usually feeling guilty for acting the way you did!

I tried to be the perfect mom, but with sons on the spectrum (who would hit, hurt, etc.) always being calm was put to the test. And, I failed. Or as I think of it now, I became more real. I yelled. Yes indeed, I yelled, screamed, cried, felt guilty, berated myself and eventually learned something. (It took awhile, mind you, but I learned!) I learned that I needed to allow myself to feel angry. When I honored this feeling, I looked at it as okay, and I stopped judging myself so much. I began to create ways to let my anger out. I let go of a lot of the judgment of feeling wrong for being angry.

I gave anger a healthy place in my life. When I got angry, instead of trying to be calm, or seem calm while still seething on the inside, I would speak about how I was feeling. I would say what I wanted to say. If I was feeling exceptionally angry and felt like I couldn't talk, I would go to the bathroom and hit a towel on the side of the tub and say what was on my mind. When the bathroom didn't feel right, I would go outside and throw rocks, hit a log on the ground, all the while saying what was bothering me. I would ramble on, and through this rambling I would end up hearing myself say something deeper, something that usually pointed at what the real problem was, like I didn't feel respected, I felt alone...

I eventually learned to end these "get your anger out sessions" with what I loved about the person I was angry at, so I could end on a positive note. Over time I learned more techniques and eventually I found myself needing to get my anger out very little. It was like I had emptied out old anger reserves. All the old anger that I never allowed myself to express had built up over the years and was now being freely released! As I did this I felt better and it was much easier to remain calm in the midst of chaos, because I had honored my anger, let it out when it needed to come out and in doing so, I let go of old anger reserves.

As you honor your anger, by letting it out and expressing it, it no longer has that beach ball effect of exploding on you at inopportune times. Instead, it becomes something you calmly and confidently express. Once expressed, you feel better, you feel heard, and then you easily move on — no guilt, no self-berating, just feeling good and at peace with yourself. That's what it's about.

Honoring your feelings applies to EVERYTHING you feel, all emotions: happy, sad, depressed, confused, feeling vulnerable, lacking confidence, worrying and feeling fearful. All of it deserves to be shared and needs to be shared. Get it out and move on. Don't stuff it! Stuffing it inside leads to the beach ball effect, getting it out creates a healthier happier you and lays the foundation for healing your child.

There's a John Mayer song called Say. I love this song. I get goose bumps every time I hear it! It's about speaking up. Play it for yourself, listen and let it be an inspiration to you to say what you need to say and feel what you need to feel!

Remember, even if what you have to say feels angry or negative, share! You MUST get it out to move onto something better — for you and your child.

E- EVERYTHING HAPPENS FOR A REASON

This one is hard for some people to swallow. You may be thinking: So you're telling me it was meant to be that my child has ADHD or some other ASD and I'm supposed to be enduring the pain and confusion that can come along with it. That's bull cr@p! How can something that feels so horrible be happening for a reason?

I get it. This is not an easy thought, and if you don't buy into it, that's okay. We're all in different places in life, with different thoughts.

Here's the thing, though. You don't have to believe in this. As a matter of fact you don't have to do anything I'm saying, I'm just sharing the mindset that helped me heal my sons. If you want to reach a higher level of clearing for your child, even if you don't fully support this, opening your mind and heart enough to explore the idea will help. If you can't, then I respect you and understand completely — I wasn't always completely supportive of this idea, so I get it. It took time for me to see differently.

What I've come to see is that everything happens for a reason. And, quite frankly, the reason is **for us to see our old patterns, and move on.** Make peace with them and move past them. To stop recreating what doesn't work and to start creating what we want.

With my belief in everything happening for a reason, here are the top three things I was able to learn from my children being on the spectrum:

Stop trying to please everyone

Stop trying to fit in and be like everyone else- be ME instead

Stop being a victim

I thought of myself as a victim many, many times along the way — probably even more then I realized. I would have moments and days of thinking, why me? Why can't my kids be as good, as well behaved, as easy as other kids? Why do I put in so much time and effort to make things better for my sons, while others seem to sit back, relax, have less to do and less stress and their kids are still doing better? At times I felt like my kids weren't considered to be as good as other kids. They weren't the teacher's favorite; they weren't the first choice for other children to invite over to their house. I even felt like we were left out of friend's and family gatherings because we as a family were too much work to have around. I felt like other parents judged me for not being a good parent — especially if my child hurt their child or had some unforeseen tantrum.

Yes, I thought these victim thoughts at times. Lucky for me I had a powerful inner feeling that told me otherwise. My kids are good enough, and my husband and I are great parents.

It took some effort for me to tap into these inner feelings of confidence though.

What I came to realize is that my sons were affected by toxins and ended up with ASDs to help me to confront my limiting thoughts- not fear and hide from them. With this understanding, I began to make peace with my past limiting thoughts. I began to see them as false ideas, just thoughts I allowed to trip me up! All false, false thoughts!

Having sons on the spectrum forced me to look at myself and my family differently. I realized as I reflected back through the years — ever since I was a child I hadn't felt confident. I was in some way trying to fit in — through my clothing, through my grades. Trying to be a good student, trying to be a good wife and mom. These were my attempts (unconsciously) to please and get positive attention, be appreciated and accepted. My need to be accepted and appreciated was, when looked at closely, something I carried around with me for years.

From my high school days of the perfect-feathered hair, to my adult days of working lots of overtime in a corporate setting, subconsciously wanting co-workers and bosses to notice how dedicated and good I was. To my mommy years of running around doing everything to serve my children in the best way possible, functioning from the place of it's not about me it's about them. Believing this thought, yet, underneath it all secretly loving it when other mothers and friends would admire how much I did for my kids. Honestly, underneath it all, when I got really honest with myself, I didn't do it all just for my kids, I was looking for outside approval, wanting others to see me as a great mom! All along the way, I was subconsciously and consciously seeking approval and appreciation.

Here's the deal: when you don't give yourself enough approval and appreciation, you look for it outside of yourself, in the form of others appreciating and approving of you!

So now, with my sons being affected by toxins, I had two wonderful human beings bringing to me the greatest lessons in life:

I'm wonderful with or without outside approval. I'm wonderful just the way I am. And, they of course, are wonderful just the way they are!

There's no need to please, to run myself ragged on the hamster wheel of to-dos just to make my children's life perfect and help everyone who asks. I can step off, stop seeking approval and love myself with or without their appreciation!

One more Big Truth I had to learn: it doesn't matter what the heck others think of me or my family. People don't know us, nor have they walked our path. On the outside they may have judged my sons for not behaving a certain way, but oh well! When I learned to let go of caring so much what others thought, my children and I grew stronger and my children really began to heal!

Everything happens for a reason: My children were meant to help me grow stronger, be more confident, speak up for them and myself. I've learned to have healthy boundaries, to say no to them and others. I've learned to treat myself as someone important. I've learned to respect myself more.

Everything happens for a reason, and quite honestly there are many more things I've learned from this healing adventure with my sons. But, if my sons had not had ASDs I may not have grown into the strong positive person I am today.

Thank you Forrest and Boden. Thank you.

L- Learn from Your Children

I previously thought my job was to teach my kids. I later learned, that while I am here to teach them, they are just as much here to **teach me.**

I have to admit, there are so many lessons that my children have taught me and continue to teach me practically everyday.

And you know what? It's usually the areas where I become the most aggravated or frustrated that my children have something to teach me. I've come to see that aggravated feeling I'm experiencing as a red flag. A flag to say there's something within me that's not happy. When I look more closely, I've seen that I'm usually angry at the fact that something I want isn't happening. I want my kids to listen to me, damn it! Why aren't they!? I want my kids to behave well — why aren't they!? Why is he being distracted and not doing what I asked or doing the opposite of what I've asked? How the heck can he speak to me disrespectfully?

Take your pick; I learned that any situation that aggravates you even in the slightest is a red flag to look at yourself. Not to blame your kids for what they have or haven't done, but to look within YOU and see why the heck you feel so aggravated.

I've noticed when I've looked more closely that my kids are a mirror of me. That everything they do, I do too. It might not be in the same context, but it does occur somewhere in my life.

It may feel hard to grasp this idea, but hang with me for a moment, hear me out.

When either of my sons has a day they don't want to take their morning vitamins, and they proceed to play, read or engage in some other activity while I call them over to take their vitamins, it feels like they're purposely ignoring me. And they probably are. When this happens, especially when we're running late, I have had times when I would get annoyed, nervous about running late, and sometimes even start to yell and say "it's time to take your vitamins . . . we have to go . . . it's time to leave for school!"

In this moment, I can think they're wrong. And allow myself to blame them for not listening. Or I can go within and see why the heck does this bother me so much? Why do my kids have to be perfect? Why must they listen to me every time, like obedient dogs? And, here's the big one: where else am I not listening to myself or to them? See, if they're my mirrors, they're showing me what I need to work on too — *that I need to listen more!*

As I've dissected this, I've come to realize yes, I want my kids to listen to me, listening is a form of respect. I want to be respected; therefore I want to be listened to. Okay. So let that part rest. But, is it okay if they don't always listen to me or immediately jump to my attention and listen when I ask them?

Yes. I have learned that I need to have grace for them. I need to be understanding that they're human and not perfect in their actions, just as I'm human and not perfect in my actions! When I look more closely I help myself to see at least three examples of where I haven't listened to them or myself.

In this open and honest self reflection, I notice there have been times when my kids called me over to see something or do something and I didn't run over immediately, I was engaged in something else and didn't allow myself to stop immediately and jump into what they wanted. Hmmm, just like they did when I called them over to take their vitamins — they were busy with something else, didn't want to stop their activity.

I look further, where else have I not listened to them? When they told me they didn't like taking their vitamins, I answered, oh well, you have to do it. I wasn't listening to them. I only listened to my urge and need to get them to take their vitamins regardless of what they wanted.

I looked further, I noticed I didn't always listen to myself (this is the mirroring effect I was mentioning.) If I went to bed earlier and didn't stay up late getting things done at night or, if I was more focused and did less in the morning I could have been on time with getting ready, which would have helped me to feel more relaxed and less rushed. If this was the case, I wouldn't have gotten mad and taken it personally that my kids weren't coming over right away to take their vitamins. So in essence, when I stayed up late taking care of to-dos, I wasn't listening to my inner self saying, "Stop being busy, go to bed now! Or let go of extra to-dos and relax, enjoy the morning getting ready with your kids. Life is not a race!"

These are just a couple of the places I wasn't listening to myself. Believe me, my list could go on and on. Let's suffice it to say, I had realized, much to my chagrin, my kids were here to teach me. To teach me what I have needed to learn for most of my life, but have been able to avoid listening to — until now. Until I decided to open my mind and think differently. Until I decided to evolve.

I'm evolving now. No, not perfect — heck no! Just more open. I've moved past a lot and honestly, my kids present me with more to evolve through.

What's important to understand is, if you're willing and open to see your lessons, the gifts of what your kids are here to teach you, you will prevail. You can live a better life that allows you to potentially heal you and your kids.

Healing is never one direction. If it is, it's not complete. Healing you and your child, now that's complete.

Anytime your child "hits one of your hot buttons" take a few moments to look inward. Where do you do the same thing to them? Where are you doing the same thing to yourself? Once you start to see this, you begin to live with more compassion and understanding for yourself and your children. This doesn't mean you condone everything they do; you're just kinder and wiser about what you draw the line with.

Yes, our kids, when we're willing to see with eyes of truth, are here to teach us!

Embracing the lessons my sons have brought to me has brought enormous healing into our lives and continues to all the time.

Exercise:

Write down one or two things that your children do that irritate you. Now think, where do you do the *same* thing? Look closely, the more honest you are with yourself, you'll find it!

Now, comes the part where you begin to cultivate more compassion. Allow yourself to see where this behavior has been helpful. Try to think of at least two examples. Apply this toward yourself and your kids.

When you start noticing that you do all the same things you judge your kids for, you begin to be more understanding. When you start to notice that these behaviors can be helpful, you begin to judge less and feel more acceptance for what is.

Knowing full well it can be tricky to view your child's poor behavior as helpful, allow me to share some examples of my own, (when my sons haven't listened to me.)

First came anger and frustration, I felt ignored.

I looked closer and realized, when I demand something instead of asking kindly, my kids can ignore me as a way of saying, "Hey you can't talk to me that way, I deserve respect." I smile because I want them to expect respect from me, other family members, friends, everyone. Yes, ignoring me was their way of helping me to learn to be kinder and more respectful to them.

I continue to look for ways that being ignored can actually be viewed as helpful. I remember that leaders don't listen to what others say and do, they follow what feels right to them. I smile knowing I'd prefer for my sons to lead rather than follow.

Hmm, where else can not listening be a good thing?

When I think of teenagers who succumb to peer pressure and do things just to fit in. I smile thinking I like the thought of my sons following what's in their hearts not what everyone else is doing.

I begin to see the positive aspect of not listening. It doesn't mean I condone not being listened to, it just means I get clear when it's important to be listened to and when it's actually a good thing that I wasn't.

Now it's your turn. See where you can find the helpful aspects of behaviors that appear to be negative.

P- PRIORITIZE YOU

If your focus has been explicitly on healing your child, wonderful, I commend you for that! How lucky your child is to have you as his or her parent. But, and here's the but: You now want to try your best to alter this mode of operating. Focusing all your attention on your child and placing yourself and your needs on the back burner is self-defeating. You help your child get so far only to find yourself tired, burned out, stressed, and feeling like you've reached a plateau in your child's healing. (Been there, done that, numerous times!) You feel lonely, confused and stinkin' frustrated that you keep putting in so much effort only to lead you to one more problem.

If you want things to get better for your child and your family, you need to take the blinders off. You want to think of your child as important. Yes, you've got that one down, you do that one well. Now here's the part that's different; **you need to think of YOURSELF as important and worthy of attention too!**

If you want to see powerful improvements in your child's life you'll need to be open and ready to step into this idea. You MUST be willing to think of yourself, otherwise, I guarantee, you and your child won't get as far as what's really possible. I don't mean to sound rude, but it's the honest truth.

LIFE BEFORE, WHEN I ONLY FOCUSED ON MY SONS

During the first few years of trying to heal and restore my sons' bodies, I did everything in my power to help them. I went to holistic doctors, pursued different therapies, shifted our food to all natural and organic and replaced our house and yard products for safer, greener all natural products. I read books on the topic, went to conferences, listened to expert speakers. I pretty much did a 360-degree shift with our lifestyle. I was probably spending 18-20 hours a day focusing on my sons — their healing and whatever I found to be best for them.

It worked for a while. My husband and I began to see results. This was promising, so I continued. Did more, pursued more, gave 150 percent of myself to the cause of healing them.

Then something went wrong.

Somewhere along the way I started feeling like cr@p. I didn't realize it, I just began to get cranky more easily. I started to feel sad and frustrated more often. I felt lonely. My husband and I began to argue more. My health was not as vibrant and balanced as it was for so many years.

I learned from our holistic doctor that I had food sensitivities and other health imbalances. I felt like cr@p.

What happened?

I was moving along at a nice clip, healing my sons, when suddenly I didn't feel so good about my life or myself any longer. What happened? I was focusing and sharing all my attention on my sons and their healing, which left zero time and attention for me. My body screamed out — NO MORE!!! Pay attention to me PLEASE! The emotional rollercoaster ride and unbalanced body were symptoms of a core problem. Lack of attention to me.

At the time, this wasn't at all obvious to me. I just thought I had to fix my health. Over time, I began to see this for what it was; I had to stop giving my all to my sons and my family. I had to be brave and give time and attention to me. Even the thought of that was scary to me. How can I do this and not be judged? How can I stop giving so much to my sons when they need my help and everyone around me will think I'm selfish? How can I give to myself and not feel selfish?

It took time, lots of reflecting and a big mindset shift to help me let go of the limiting ideas and thoughts that kept me tied to thinking I had to dedicate myself to my family.

THE RESULT OF LOOSENING THE REIGNS OF THE SUPERMOM MINDSET

By letting go of some of my Supermom Mindset, the idea I had to fix everything, do everything for my family and be completely selfless about it, I opened up an entirely new level of healing in my family's life.

I began to feel good. No, make that GREAT! I was allowing myself pleasure. I was feeling invigorated. I was exercising, eating whole foods, taking supplements, going out with friends, making more time for dates with my husband, expressing myself creatively. I was feeling awesome! My health began to balance, my sons conditions', which had somewhat plateaued, now improved. They too were feeling the effects of mom feeling awesome!

When mom feels good, the entire family benefits. When mom feels good for an extended period of time, the dynamics of the family begin to improve. When mom feels good, dad and mom have a much better chance at getting along, arguments decrease and love is more easily exchanged.

What does this mean for your kids?

Giving to yourself, paying attention to yourself as someone who really matters, creates healing, in the deepest, most profound ways possible. More than any supplement, herb, or latest holistic cream can provide.

Paying attention to yourself is a vital ingredient in clearing ASDs.

Summary of the HELP Heal Mindset

So now you're privy, quite honestly, to the mindset that has helped me heal my sons. Because I went beyond placing ALL my emphasis on their needs and stepped outside of that very comfortable and familiar (and easily accepted) mode of operating, I met with a success unimaginable. My sons, and I and my family are all much better off for it!

Going forward, a great approach to creating the highest level of healing and the most wonderful level of living for your children, begins with acquiring the HELP Heal Mindset.

Acquiring the HELP Heal Mindset builds a strong foundation for clearing ASDs. To be honest, if you choose to follow the 7 RESTORE Keys I lay out in this book or if you choose to pursue a different approach, it's all good! I do want to place emphasis on the fact that if you integrate the HELP Heal Mindset into ANY approach, you increase your chances of getting further with clearing your child of their ASD. Your potential to make a significant difference in their lives skyrockets with this mindset. The HELP Heal Mindset is that powerful!

The HELP Heal Mindset helped me to clinch the deal with healing my sons but, there still were other **integral components** to clearing my sons.

I sat down one day and decided to summarize what these key steps were which had such an impact on clearing my sons' autism.

Through this process I uncovered seven keys. I refer to these as the **7 RESTORE Keys.**

Yup, another acronym. =)

The 7 RESTORE Keys

R- Reality Rewritten

E- Eat All Natural Real Food

S- Simple Daily Body Cleanse

T- Thrive in Natural Balanced Environments

O- "Om", Listen to Your Intuition

R- Respect and Appreciate Yourself

E- Establish Balance in Key Areas of Life

Might not sound like much, but I assure you, when these 7 RESTORE Keys are followed, they can have a powerful impact on improving your child's life.

I still, to this day, if something goes slightly astray with my sons' bodies, will take a step back, and think to myself, "Ok, which RESTORE Key do I need to place more emphasis on? What Key will help restore optimal functioning to their bodies and behaviors?"

We as a family live the 7 RESTORE Keys, but like any human being, we get out of sync sometimes, do things that don't always serve us best, and so, when this occurs, I check in with my RESTORE Keys and spot exactly what we need to do next to bring everyone back into balance. When it's your lifestyle it can become second nature. And, bringing balance to everyone's body happens that much more quickly.

The 7 RESTORE Keys are game changers. They summarize my healing journey with my sons and, in one quick snapshot, convey exactly what you can do if you want to recreate the results I achieved. Cleared autism.

RESTORE KEY R

REALITY REWRITTEN

CREATE A NEW STORY

My child has ASDs is probably not the story you'd like to continue living. That means you need to begin by telling yourself a new story.

I *had* to do this in order to make progress with my sons!

You need to get clear on what you want for yourself and your family and begin moving toward that.

It's time to give yourself permission to live differently and have new and better feeling experiences in your life.

Allow me to explain further:

Your life is a story. The way things have played out thus far has everything to do with the story you've told yourself. Someone who thinks they deserve a lot of wealth and acts on this attracts lots of wealth. Someone who believes he can become a great actor, becomes a great actor. Anything we believe in — and I mean *truly believe in* — and then act on, we find our life experiences reflecting.

The same holds true for the less satisfying stories people have told themselves — *I can't do it, I'm afraid to do it, I'm not good enough, my kids don't fit in, they're not the same as other kids…* and on and on…

When people are young they have experiences that impress thoughts into their heads. These ideas don't always help them be their best or trust that they deserve to have a life that's easy and great.

Maybe you had parents that argued all the time, or told you that you didn't try hard enough, or you were constantly being forced to look your best— these situations can plant seeds, seeds that instill in a person the wrong ideas about themselves. *You're not perfect enough, you don't do enough, you don't deserve to have a peaceful harmonious family life because you didn't grow up with that.*

These ideas can come from parents, teachers, family, friends, television, and the media. People then inadvertently live their lives from this misconception about themselves. This misconception is certainly **not the truth**, but, nonetheless guides their choices and actions. Until they question it and **decide** to follow a different story, a different set of beliefs.

It's that simple. We can change our lives, our future, simply by allowing ourselves to create a new story about ourselves and what we deserve. There's a saying by Henry Ford that sums it up: "If you think you can, you can, if you think you can't, you can't."

There's another force at work here and it's called Universal Law.

Universal Law

The Law of the Universe shows us that *like attracts like* or as Dr. Drew Rozell, coach and author of A Very Cool Life Code (www.VeryCoolLife. com), and many other wise influential individuals, such as Albert Einstein, Deepak Chopra, Bernard Beckwith have conveyed: *like energy attracts like energy.*

As we know, everything is made up of energy. Your body, your house, this book. Anything and everything is energy. Even your thoughts are made up of energy. We have MRIs and PET scans, which have shown us that thoughts are energy, they're measurable brainwaves.

This leads us to see that as our thoughts are energy and energy vibrates, the vibration of our thoughts then go out into the world, only to attract back to us the same level of vibration or energy. When you think certain thoughts you attract like energy or like *circumstances* in your life to reflect your thinking.

Ever think to yourself, "Today is a good day." What you then see unfold in your day is what you would consider to be a good day. Likewise, the flipside of that holds true. When you think your day isn't too terrific, you attract experiences that have you feeling cruddy about your day.

Like energy attracts like energy. Therefore, any thoughts you think will attract like experiences in your life.

How Does this Apply to My Family and Our Situation?

Those of you reading this book who have children with ASDs may be saying, *No, I did not consciously think about my son or daughter having an ASD. How can this apply to me?*

It's true you may not have consciously thought this, but somewhere along the way you acquired a thought — from your parents, family, friends, whomever that had you thinking you were different, you weren't good enough, you didn't fully fit in, whatever that thinking may be. That thinking was stored into your subconscious and has then allowed you to attract whatever experiences in your life that resonated with not feeling good enough.

So you're right, you may not have consciously had this thought, but this thought is *in you* guiding your actions and reactions to things in your life and, *attracting to you the exact experiences you have in your life right now!* Look around you. If you have children with an ASD you have been living from an old misconceived thought that *you are not good enough or you are different from others.*

If this thought makes you feel defensive, that's okay. It's normal to get defensive about something that hits home for us. Take a day or two and sit with this concept if you need to. Look around at your life, notice where this may be true. Or, if this idea repels you completely, you're welcome to get your money back for this book. If you're open to this concept, let's continue.

With the understanding that you have been operating consciously or subconsciously with the idea you are not good enough in some way, it's time now to change that thought, to change *your* story.

You'll want to start thinking more loving supportive thoughts about yourself, which we'll get to in the second RESTORE Key R- Respect & Appreciate Yourself.

In the meanwhile, let's start with simply creating a new story. Setting up the outline for the new life you deserve to live with your family. For the new life you'd like to attract.

Step one:
Write down the future you want for yourself and your family. Now, I don't mean what you think right now is possible, I mean what you really, really want for yourself and your family. If you could choose an ideal life, what would you be doing? Would your children be healed? How would they be acting? How would you and your family be getting along? What would your days look like — how much free time would you have? How would you feel? Where would you live? Get into the space of, if I could live my dream, this is what it would look like. Get into details. Give yourself

permission to go to thoughts you may have not allowed yourself to go to before.

Once you identify what you really want, write it all down. This is your new story, your revised future, the future that is possible for you, not a fairy tale but what you ultimately deserve in this lifetime. If you can dream it, it can be.

I imagined my kids to be healed from their ASDs and so it is now. But, I couldn't have gotten there if I didn't take the time to "see" and believe something better was possible.

Once you complete this exercise, read your story aloud. Read it to your spouse or partner, read it to your children. Begin to imagine what it would be like to live this way.

If you ever want to attract and create this new story, you need to believe it's possible. One way to start to believe it's possible is to focus 5 minutes of your time each day daydreaming, imaging — visualizing this new life for yourself.

If you start thinking and imaging this new life for yourself even just 5 minutes a day, you begin to align with new possibilities, possibilities that align with what you would really love to experience in this lifetime with your family.

Set up a consistent time to daydream. Visualize your new life. Setting up a consistent time, like immediately after lunch or right when you wake up in the morning, etc., lends itself to making it easier to follow through on doing this each day. The more you do this, the easier it will be.

The more you do this, the more great things you begin to attract into your life. This exercise helps your mindset shift from what's wrong in your life to what's possible for your life.

Some people find it difficult to visualize what they want. I have been in the same boat. Here's what I did to help myself out in this arena: Every time I came across an image in a magazine that I was really moved by, it depicted a feeling: happiness, freedom, connecting, or anything that made me feel good, I ripped it out and added it to a folder. I kept the folder in a place I would be certain to see, perusing it's contents a few times a week. I would flip through the folder and pull out whatever image caught my attention. These images were the jumping-off point for my imagination to run wild, to really get into the space of being a part of my new life — my new story.

If you want to start the journey of strengthening and restoring your child's body from autism and other ASDs, you want and need to get into the space of how it would feel and what it would be like to live an ideal life. Think of it as retraining your brain and your thoughts to expect and attract something better for yourself and your family — something magnificent!

For anyone reading this book who thinks this step may be difficult, I understand. When you deal with ASDs day in and day out, it will affect you emotionally. You might not feel like it's truly possible to live a new and better life, never mind trying to get into the space of imaging this new and better life. If this is you, take heart. I've been in this place before, on and off for a while, but allow me to add, if you want something different for your children and yourself, you NEED to apply this step. This step CAN NOT be skipped. If you bypass this step you will find it much more difficult to come to a place of clearing ASDs.

So, please, please, get into that space of creating a new story for yourself — the story that you and your family deserve to live!

RESTORE KEY E

EAT NATURAL REAL FOODS

What Foods Qualify as Real and Natural

Food affects people's bodies immensely. Not only does it impact someone's weight and contribute to their overall health, it affects their moods and their behaviors.

I've seen the power that food can have on people's behaviors, time and again, with the immediate examples of both my kids and myself.

Recently, we went to New York City to celebrate my oldest son's 11th birthday. He invited his best friend.

One of the things he chose to do on this day was visit FAO Schwartz, a famous toy store. This store had half a floor designated to candy, and my son asked if he could get something. He and his friend were eyeing a gummy bear 7 inches tall! Normally I would have looked for something more wholesome and natural. But, on this special day, with his best friend along and knowing how far Forrest has come — his body being very strong now, very clean and very capable of handling some junk — I said okay, but I asked if he could eat only a little of it.

He agreed and happily bought his first-ever giant gummy bear.
That day, things went well. His mood was upbeat, he felt good and comfortable.

The next day, he was a little tired and off, but nothing unexpected after such a big day. But days two and three after his New York adventure, Forrest was crying, getting very emotional over little things, getting frustrated and impatient easily and acting disrespectful.

What was this all about? I suspected red dye, artificial flavors and any other chemicals he may have consumed in that gummy bear, detoxing from his body.

Yup, when chemicals and junk are in the body they very often affect a person's emotions and behaviors, making them more easily upset, angry, sad, and impatient.

This is exactly what I experienced with Forrest and I remember thinking to myself, wow, I haven't seen Forrest act like this in ages—thank God.

Forrest having some of that giant gummy bear was a good thing on several levels — he got to have fun with a friend and he got to notice how it made him feel when the junk that entered his body was trying to leave his body. He became aware of how food was impacting his behavior.

What we eat and serve to our kids has a huge impact on all of us. Diet was one of the first things I changed for my sons. When I first learned there might be something off for my sons, I called a DAN (Defeat Autism Now) doctor, spoke to an assistant there and learned very quickly what foods to begin shifting my sons away from and which to replace them with. I received a crash course over the phone how to start the process.

In the days, weeks and months that followed I read more, went through trial and error. I found foods that worked, some that didn't. Some that tasted good, some that tasted like crud!

The result? Over time, my sons' behaviors, temper tantrums and anger decreased significantly (not entirely, but significantly.) There was a large enough impact to warrant us making this our new way of eating. I would do anything to make life better for them and us as a family. This definitely contributed to more harmony in our family. I was hooked!

What did I uncover through this trial and error process and my eventual return to nutrition school? **The more natural and real the food is you choose to eat, the better it is for you and your kids.**

It's that simple.

WHAT FOODS ARE BETTER FOR YOU TO EAT

Veggies and Fruits- Good ol' fashion veggies and fruits, straight from a garden, a farmer's market or local farm stand. The fresher the better. When your food is fresh there's more live energy and nutrients to transfer to you and your child's bodies.

If you're unable to get the fruits and veggies fresh, no biggie, go with what's available at the supermarket. Some veggies in your family's diet are much better than no veggies.

High Quality Protein– beans, legumes, nuts, chicken, fish, and small amounts of red meat. It's preferred that animal protein is organic when possible, but antibiotic free and steroid free at least.

Whole Grains– grains like brown rice, quinoa, millet, amaranth and oats.

By the way, there's a lot of marketing going on out there that touts lots of products are whole grain! Be aware, read labels, most breads, crackers, bagels and pastas are NOT whole grain. Once you take a grain and grind it into a flour, the grain is no longer whole. A whole grain has it's hull- exterior intact and has more nutrients to offer your child's body. A good example is brown rice versus white rice. Brown rice has its exterior intact. White rice has been processed and refined and it no longer has its exterior, which is where most nutrients are found.

High Quality Water– what would be considered high quality drinking water? Water directly from a natural spring. Of course, not all of us have easy access to a natural spring, so the next best water to drink would be spring water in a glass bottle. Again, not everyone has the means to buy glass bottled spring water, so the next in succession would be reverse osmosis water. You can purchase a reverse osmosis system for your home. This is the granddaddy of all filtration systems and will produce the best, cleanest water possible aside from spring water. Other filtration systems won't necessarily do as thorough of a job. We want to keep those chemicals and toxins out of your child's body (and your entire family's body) so a filtration system that does most of the job, but not all of the job, isn't adequate. Landing below a heavy-duty filtration system comes plastic bottled spring water. Not as good as the other options, but when the other options aren't as feasible, this is the best option.

My family and I have had Poland Springs water delivered to us monthly. It may not be the absolute highest quality water, but it still is good quality water, and it's a huge improvement over our tap water.

Allow me to diverge here for a moment, just to share the importance of water.

When Boden was in kindergarten, he began to digress with his behavior, this was after he had been improving and doing so well. I wasn't 100% sure why, but began to change more things in his diet and with supplements to create more balance. I always sensed that I just needed to create more balance within his body in order to shift the symptoms or behaviors occurring in class. Over time this began to happen.

The major thing I changed? I began to send clean spring water to school with Boden. See, in his class they would serve pitchers of tap water at snack time to the children. He was drinking tap water almost everyday. Originally I thought to myself it wasn't a big deal. Eventually, I decided maybe it was a bigger deal than I realized.

As I began to make sure Boden drank only high quality water, his negative behaviors began to decrease.

The following year, when he started first grade, a teacher said to me, "What was all that hoopla I heard about Boden from last year? He's a wonderful boy to have in class, I don't understand what they were talking about."

Hmmm, how cool is that?!!

Clean water and real food are more powerful than one might think!

WHY IS NATURAL FOOD BETTER FOR YOU?

Well, for several reasons.

For starters, natural organic food is chock full of nutrients. Organic produce has been tested and shown to have up to 75% more nutrients than conventionally grown produce.

When humans came into existence, we ate only all natural real food. Cave men didn't go out to their local store and buy some packaged crackers and a box of cereal to eat. They ate natural plants and berries and ate fresh animal protein.

Throughout the course of history, we humans have been feeding our bodies natural foods, because that's what works for us, that's what our bodies were meant to eat. Then we discovered preservatives and other additives that allowed us to more cheaply make our food taste good as well as stretch the length of time our food could sit around on a shelf before we bought and ate it.

These foreign additions to our food were never necessary to our existence, nor are they helpful to our health. Real, natural food is what is necessary for our wellbeing.

Our children need natural food feeding their bodies, cells, tissues and organs.

By providing your child's body with real food, you help their bodies to begin the process of cleaning out the gunk and toxic stuff that's filled their cups — remember all that toxic stuff they were inadvertently exposed to before you had a true understanding of what is most helpful to them and what isn't.

Real, all-natural food is clean food. Clean food helps the body to strengthen itself, and aids in the cleansing and clearing process. Yes, there are many foods that aid in de-toxing a person's body. The more natural food you put into your child's body, the more of an opportunity their body has to keep emptying that cup and cleansing out some of the toxins that created their ASD conditions to begin with.

Natural real foods are phenomenal for your child's body because they're full of live enzymes, vitamins and minerals. Think of real food as a little powerhouse of potential ASD-clearing qualities.

Children with ADHD or any ASD tend to be nutrient deficient. Feeding your child real food will only help bring more balance to their bodies, aid-ing in replenishing those nutrient deficiencies. When nutrient deficiencies are balanced, some of those behaviors your child previously experienced begin to subside.

You know the saying "You are what you eat." Well that saying holds true. You and your child are what you eat. If you put junk in you'll get junk out. What do I mean by this?

If You Put Junk in You'll Get Junk Out

If your child eats junk food, food with artificial flavors and preservatives, they will be more apt to feel like junk and act like junk. Same goes for you— eat junk and you'll have a tendency to overreact to your child's actions. (Been there, done that a few hundred times.)

I try to keep this equation in mind:
Junk in = junk attitudes and behaviors.
Healthy real food in = healthy moods and behaviors.

Keep Your Food Simple

Goal:

When it comes to packaged processed foods go for very few ingredients and ingredients you're familiar with. If you read an ingredient label and you don't know what something is or it has a long list of ingredients, put it down. It will detract from clearing out your child's body and will honestly only enable more ASD behaviors.

Think of my son Forrest — red gummy bear- emotional and moody, no gummy bear- more balanced in his responses and honestly easier to get along with.

Yes, keep your food simple.

If you want to buy processed foods look for those that have fewer ingredients.

This is easier than it sounds. You'll want to get comfortable with reading labels. No, I don't mean looking to see how many grams of fat or sodium a food has. I recommend you skip looking at that information altogether! I tell my clients to place their hand over the numbers and read only the ingredients. Remember, you're looking for quality real foods.

This means if you read a label and you understand what all the ingredients are— walnuts, apples, water, cinnamon, etc. — you're in great shape, this product is more wholesome and will therefore work better for your child.

If the ingredient list contains things you've never heard of – food additives, preservatives and other chemical sounding names, then skip that food altogether!

If the ingredient list is a paragraph long, that food isn't all that terrific for your child either. Too many foods squeezed into one product means that food is teetering on the edge of being less natural — how many things grow in the soil and have 35 ingredients? Too many ingredients in one product can be difficult for your child's body to digest.

Quick recap with label reading: Look for fewer ingredients and ingredients that you are familiar with. It's that easy!!

FOODS THAT CAN AGGRAVATE ADHD AND ALL ASDS

Gluten & Dairy

Children with ADHD or any ASD function better without gluten and dairy in their diet. And, I want to share a secret with you — just about everybody will feel better, act better and think more clearly without dairy and gluten in their diet. (Just sayin'!!)

Why is this? In general gluten is sticky and difficult for people's digestive tracts to process.

Secondly, when it comes to a child with ASDs, his or her digestive tract has usually been impaired to some degree by toxins. As a result, their digestive tract is not as strong and can leak food particles into the bloodstream (also known as Leaky Gut Syndrome.) These food particles, once in the bloodstream act like opiates, creating an array of symptoms ranging from difficulty focusing, hyperactivity, anger, impatience to more physical symptoms, such as stomach discomfort, constipation or diarrhea, etc...

Additionally, the digestive enzymes that break down gluten and dairy are very often impaired. When a child then consumes dairy or gluten, they're not able to fully digest these foods. These undigested food particles can then lead to an assortment of symptoms- mood swings, hyperactivity, low energy, lack of focus, compulsive behaviors, cravings, depression, rashes, ear infections, heartburn, irregular bowel movements and much more!

Food Sensitivity

Additionally, when someone's cup has been filled with toxins, their immune system begins to create antibodies to fight some of the foods they're eating. When a persons' body fights the food that it's eating this is referred to as a **food sensitivity**, and this food sensitivity can show up in an array of ways: It can cause the body to experience moodiness, difficulty focusing, weight gain, weight loss, hyperactivity and any of the symptoms listed above.

Food sensitivities are different from food allergies. A food allergy is more obvious; it's a reaction that occurs within minutes of someone eating an offending food. As in when someone eats a banana and their throat begins to swell minutes later, or their skin breaks out with hives.

Food sensitivities are a delayed reaction to an offending food. This means someone can eat something they're sensitive to and not experience a reaction until 3 hours later or up to 5 days later. The symptoms can last up to 14-21 days.

In the first several months after switching our sons over to gluten free foods, we had family over for dinner. I had made a batch of wheat pasta for our company and while I was making a batch of gluten-free pasta, my son Forrest sauntered over to the counter, reached up into the wheat pasta bowl, pulled out a handful of pasta, and happily stuffed it into his mouth. Before I could get over to him, he quickly reached up and stuffed a second handful of pasta into his mouth. By the time I reached him, he had chewed and swallowed a good portion of the pasta. So I said to myself, "Oh well, we shall see what happens."

The following day, Forrest was fine. The second day after eating the pasta with gluten Forrest was still fine — no different behaviors, all was well. On the third day, things changed. Forrest began to have a spontaneous explosion of anger and temper tantrums. He did this on and off for five days. And then, it disappeared. What was this heightened behavior all about?

Forrest had a sensitivity to gluten.

His reaction didn't show up right away. Instead, it appeared as though he was okay with eating gluten (at first), but we learned from this experience that his reaction tends to surface approximately three days after consumption of gluten and the behavior it induces can last anywhere from three to five days.

This is just one small example of a food sensitivity and the impact it may have on your child's body and behaviors.

Go Slow with Diet Changes

Of course, it's easy for me to say, "Oh and by the way your child and your whole family would benefit greatly, and you'll help ease ASD symptoms in your child, by changing to a gluten free and dairy free diet." This is a huge undertaking and it's worth more time and explanation. Take a deep breath and let yourself know you don't have to make the switch immediately.

Lets make this easier: Suggestion: Begin small. Don't worry about eating everything gluten and dairy free right away. As a matter of fact, don't worry about it at all for now. Instead, focus on bringing in two new real food products and one new vegetable into your family's diet. After two weeks of eating these new foods look for a few new gluten free products. Go slow and easy. Trying to change everything at once leads to feeling overwhelmed. And when you feel overwhelmed, you don't do anything. So, keep it small and simple. You'll get further.

One More Food to Think About

Sugar!

Yes, sugar is something that can exacerbate your child's ASD symptoms. I'm not suggesting you take sugar out of your child's diet entirely and forever. Though if you choose to do so, you would be making some amazing differences in his or her life.

To be more realistic, try taking a lot of sugar out. Why? Because sugar (sucrose) depletes the body of nutrients.

When someone eats sugar they're eating a food devoid of nutrients. In order for sugar to be digested, it depletes your body of some of your existing nutrients. A body depleted of nutrients isn't balanced. This can lead to more pronounced ASD behaviors.

Sugar can also cause your body to produce high levels of insulin fast, leading to hyperactivity, difficulty focusing and later when your insulin crashes, tiredness, grouchiness and food cravings.

Life without sugar, no way you say?

Well, here's what my family and I did. Initially I stopped giving my kids processed cane sugar. I gave them foods and products with **alternative natural sweeteners like maple sugar, agave, brown rice syrup, molasses, palm sugar,** etc. I would bake things with only alternative natural sweeteners. Everything tasted just as good.

After several months, we introduced sugar again. They could have it in small quantities and seemed okay.

Since then, my sons now have sugar, but I make an effort to bypass it when we can.

The main idea here is to attempt to bypass sugar for a while. Introduce it later, but be mindful of it going forward. Don't totally deprive yourself or your kids though — that NEVER feels good! =)

Just to reiterate RESTORE Key E — Eat all natural real foods as much as possible and you will help your child lay a foundation for clearing some ASD symptoms.

A little side note:

Initially I was shifting my sons' diet but didn't apply any diet changes to my husband or myself.
It wasn't until I applied what I was learning at school and began to make better food for the **whole family** that we *all* began to feel better.

As you follow this RESTORE key, remember to apply these eating habits to everyone- your kids, yourself and your spouse or partner if he or she is game. You'll just see better results if you do!

By the way, if for some reason your spouse or partner won't switch eating habits, that's okay. Let them do what's right for them. If they're not forced into it, there's a good chance over time they may join you in your improved eating approach.

I HEALED MY SONS OF AUTISM AND YOU CAN TOO:

RESTORE KEY S

SIMPLE DAILY BODY CLEANSE

WHY WOULD YOU AND YOUR FAMILY WANT TO CLEAN TOXINS OUT OF YOUR BODY?

While at a conference, Sidney Baker, M.D. a pioneer of the DAN (Defeat Autism Now) biomedical treatments shared a story about one of his young patients. The parents of this patient called him and said their son was acting extremely aggressive and they weren't able to calm him down. The parents were distressed, and after talking with them, Dr. Baker discovered that the child hadn't had a bowel movement in over a week. Dr. Baker made some suggestions. After following them, the parents noticed a major difference in their son's behavior. When they next spoke to Dr. Baker they were pleased to share that their son was doing significantly better. His aggression dropped dramatically once he had a bowel movement.

Bowel movements are just one way our bodies naturally clear out toxins.

Quite simply, children on the spectrum and parents of children on the spectrum tend to have a more difficult time excreting toxins from their bodies.

Here's the deal: Our bodies are naturally built to clean themselves out everyday. It's the natural way. We eat, breathe in, and absorb through our skin different substances and foods every single day. Our bodies are amazing machines that take in all of these foods and substances, absorb and break down what they need and excrete the rest.

Our bodies can do this quite well when they're in a state of balance. If our bodies are in a state of imbalance, which is the case with children on the spectrum and their parents, it's more difficult for our bodies to perform this function.

Children's bodies with ASDs have been largely impacted by toxins, to a degree in which their regular detox functions don't work as well as they could. As for the parents of a child on the spectrum, the level of stress that they experience; extreme concern for their child or contending with more extreme behaviors, etc. can lead to weakening of their body's natural detox functions.

Solution? Make an effort to clean the body out through simple powerful means everyday!

Clean the Body Out: Get Movin'

It's important for you and your family to move your bodies everyday! It doesn't have to be a complicated exercise program. If you like that, great, go for it! If not, just find some sort of movement that feels good and *do it!*

If you can get outside with your family, even better. Fresh air and nature really add to the healing equation, when it comes to balancing ASDs and your body too (more to come on this topic in RESTORE Key T).

I attended a school convention in Miami a few years back. It was a blast! I spent time learning, growing and partying with friends. Miami just beckons partying, so I obliged. Well, after a night of socializing, dancing and drinking, I awoke to find myself feeling tired and very foggy brained. I got out of bed and dressed in my running clothes, put on my trusty sneakers and out the hotel door I went. I headed right down to the beach where I proceeded to jog for a couple of miles. It wasn't easy, I could feel myself feeling tight and moving much slower than usual, but I did it. When I was through, I stretched for a few minutes. As I headed back to my hotel room I noticed a marked difference. I felt lighter. My focused thinking was back and my energy was pretty good! Why? Simply because I took the time to move my body. Had I skipped jogging, I would have probably remained in a fog and acted grouchy for the entire day.

When you and your family exercise and move, you allow your bodies to release toxins.

The goal is very much to release toxins.

Why?

Because ASD symptoms can and probably will increase if your kids don't move around much. Additionally, the whole family will be more prone to feeling tired, grouchy, have difficulty thinking, and more than likely think negative thoughts.

ASD symptoms become more pronounced when your children don't move their bodies.

As you and the family get out there and move your bodies, you do more than just stretch your muscles and slim down your waistline. Yes, these things are happening, but in addition to this, you are also helping stagnant energy move. You shift and release blockages that can occur from ingesting toxins like junk food, the pesticides a neighbor sprayed on his lawn, etc...

Moving enables you to physically detoxify all this stuff from your body. Your lymph nodes are stimulated and will drain the buildup of toxins when cardio movement is involved. When you move enough to work up a sweat, you release and eliminate toxins through your skin. And, when you move, your colon is given that extra push to eliminate yesterday's meal.

Elson M. Haas, M.D., shares in his book *The New Detox Diet*: "Exercise is very important to support the cleansing process. It helps to relax the body, clears wastes, and prevents toxicity symptoms."

What are toxicity symptoms?

They're signs that your body contains an excess of toxins.

Take a look below to see some of the signs and symptoms of toxicity. Notice if you or your children experience any of these.

Headaches	Nervousness	Backaches
Insomnia	Anxiety	Bad breath
Constipation	Indigestion	Fever
Mood changes	Coughs	Hives
Depression	Joint pains	Fatigue
Pimples	Tight or stiff neck	Skin rashes
Sinus congestion	Environmental sensitivity	

This list was provided by Elson M. Haas, M.D., and is only a partial list, to see more, go to *The New Detox Diet* book.

When you release toxins (or empty your cup), you will notice moods improve- feeling and acting calmer and more focused. Skin conditions clear and illness improves.

As you can see, movement is essential to you and your family's well-being!

Here are some of the ways my family and I move our bodies. Some of these activities we do together, some we do separately:
- Dancing
- Playing sports in our backyard
- Yoga
- Jogging
- Trampoline

- Walking
- Hiking
- Hockey
- Tennis

I recommend that you find a form of movement that feels good for you and your kids, not something you force yourself to do. It needs to be pleasurable for you to want to engage in it. Otherwise, you'll probably bypass exercising all together. Remember, it can be as simple as going for a walk everyday, playing in the backyard as a family or as involved as taking a dance or gymnastics class.

Hint: figure out what sounds the most fun and appealing to you and the easiest, and go for that! The less complicated you make it, the easier it will be to continue to make it a regular part of your life!

CLEAN THE BODY OUT: DRINK LOTS OF WATER

It's also highly imperative that along with moving your body, you drink plenty of water. Yes, moving your body allows you to release counter-productive toxins, but really, in order to fully flush these toxins from the body, you'll want to drink six-to-eight glasses of water (for adults) and at least four glasses for your child. Do this each and every day. There's no way around it. Exercise and skip the water intake and you'll notice you and your children still won't feel all that terrific. Exercise and drink lots of water and guess what — yes, you guys have a much better chance of feeling great!

Water hydrates you, water fortifies all of your cells, water helps you eliminate toxins and think more clearly. Water can even improve your moods. When I get cranky sometimes, I think, oh time for a glass of water. Our bodies are comprised of mostly water, and we need lots of it to keep all systems functioning at maximum potential.

One way to get more water into you and your family's body: pour a cup of water and add some fresh fruit like lemons, limes or berries for extra flavor or a splash of fresh fruit juice. Still doesn't sound appealing? Drink seltzer water with only natural flavors added. There are lots of seltzer waters out there, read the labels and find a brand with only high quality ingredients added.

When it comes to drinking water, just a reminder — go for the highest quality water you can!

CLEAN THE BODY OUT: IT'S TIME TO POOP!

Right in line with moving your body and drinking more water comes emptying your colon of yesterday's meal — that means having at least one bowel movement per day.

Yep, that's right, one poop a day, at minimum! When your body holds onto food or really, pardon the pun here, the crap that's left over from your food after the nutrients and good stuff have been extracted and utilized by your system, what's left is all the toxic stuff. If this leftover stuff (your poop) is allowed to sit in your body for too long, a backup occurs and this backup causes toxins to begin to circulate in your system, instead of going out the back door. These toxins can leave a person feeling tired, angry, depressed, nervous, worried, or create pimples, rashes, stomach bloating, etc. Blah, blah, blah, you get the gist!

Naturally release all that excrement from the body once a day. Yes, make sure your family is pooping!

Clean the Body Out: Use Supplements and Food

What else can you do to further help your family clean out their bodies and poop every day?

Take at least one **probiotic** (good bacteria) a day. Recommended brands: Garden of Life- Primal Defense, Theralac, or Kirkman's- Multiflora.

Take one-to-six teaspoons (depending on severity) of **liquid magnesium** a day.

Liquid chlorella is an awesome addition to your arsenal of cleansing tactics. I use 1-2 teaspoons a day for my sons and myself. We use Detox-ND by Premier Research Labs.

Aloe Vera juice is also a helpful supplement for supporting bowel movements.

Lemon Water- Other options to support elimination: Upon waking, drink one cup of warm water with the juice from half a lemon in it. Or, take **psyllium seeds,** two-to-four teaspoons or 8-12 caps a day.

When my kids hit a bump in the road with healing and some new symptom surfaced, I would always try to go back to the basics. Okay, is everyone pooping everyday and is everyone drinking enough water? More often than not, I would find my kids were drinking barely any water. When I made it a habit to remind them at certain times of the day to drink a glass of water, I noticed it helped their new symptoms improve.

Toxins create symptoms, symptoms show us the body is imbalanced. Release toxins and decrease symptoms (ASD symptoms that is!)

ANOTHER CLEANSING APPROACH

I rely on these approaches to help clean my sons' bodies, as well as my own, but initially when I first started the healing process for them, a holistic doctor helped to give them what I consider a "jump start" with detoxing.

What I mean is this: When we first started seeing a holistic doctor, she suggested we do a stronger detox process, something that would allow their bodies to expel the toxins from various sources not only in their bloodstream, but from stored areas in tissues and organs. We obliged and found ourselves using topical lotions. We did this on and off for several months while being monitored by the holistic doctor.

What I found were results that were simply amazing. Really, I say this from my heart! Forrest who was having difficulty being calm and focused now was sitting playing with toys quietly, for great lengths of time.

Boden, who had lost motor coordination was going to physical therapy to aid the process of learning to walk, was now moving his legs much more easily. His physical therapist even said to me, "I don't know what you've been doing but he's doing awesome." His left leg, once difficult for him to move, is now moving much more easily.

You can't go out and buy this lotion over the counter; it needs to be prescribed by a holistic doctor. If you want to jumpstart the cleansing process as my family and I did, I recommend you find a DAN doctor or another holistic doctor who's familiar with detoxing and begin working with them.

Keep in mind though, any work your family does with a holistic practitioner is further enhanced when you simply follow the basics: move, drink water, poop everyday and take supplements if need be!

RESTORE KEY T

THRIVE IN NATURAL BALANCED ENVIRONMENTS

Our New Home

Eight years ago, my family and I moved into a new home. It was newly built, beautiful and it reflected a lot of our own personal ideas. We were thrilled to move in.

At the time, I had absolutely zero idea that there was anything I needed to be cautious of regarding my sons, my husband and I. What would we need to be concerned about? We had this great new house that should have been worry-free for years.

I was oblivious to the fact that having built our home with standard building materials meant that it was not as healthy as it could have been. So much of what our house was built from was unhealthy for us, especially our sons. After being educated by an environmental interior designer, I learned that when you have new factory-produced carpet, new kitchen cabinets, new sealed hardwood floors or freshly painted walls, all these elements are emitting gases as they harden and age. These fumes, inhaled over time, begin to fill a person's cup. When this happens, your body and regular functioning is affected. And too many toxins can cause ADHD, autism or any ASD.

Avoid my mistake; do the opposite of what I did. If you're building a new home, try incorporating more natural products. If you already built your home with less natural products as we did, you can invest in some terrific air filters. Not just any air filters, but the types that do a terrific job purifying out-gassing from formaldehyde and paint. NEEDS.com is a great resource we have used to purchase our air filters. We use Aireox brand air filters.

Seven-to-10 years after a house is built, the out-gassing process is pretty much complete. If you have a home older than 10 years, you're in good shape, provided you haven't painted or added on more recently. If so, air filters make a difference.

Going forward you'll want to look around your home, yard, car and all living spaces in which you spend a substantial amount of time. Are they natural, or could they use some sprucing up, so to speak?

My family and I never used all-natural organic cleaning products, laundry detergent, air fresheners and paint until we needed to. We learned that if we wanted our sons to heal and clear entirely, we would need to provide them with natural balanced living environments. The more natural and balanced our living environments, the better our children's healing chances.

When we sleep, our liver is hard at work cleansing and clearing our body. If our environment is continuously out-gassing toxins, our liver is working overtime. Eventually, it may be difficult for our liver to process everything, so some of these toxins get stored (this is our cup filling up). Having natural, fume-free living spaces allows a child's body a chance to relax, detox out some of the old garbage and work on replenishing and rebuilding strong robust cells, tissues and organs.

Remember, as you keep in mind going more natural, you'll want to look around not only at your home, but your yard and your car as well.

There are many options of all-natural products to use. If you want to keep it simple you can always buy vinegar, baking soda and tea tree oil and use these to clean just about your entire home. Or, you can march down to your local health food store or a grocery store and purchase all-natural cleaning products.

Remember all natural grass and plant fertilizers too, what you and your kids tread on comes into the house.

A great resource for all natural products for your home (and baby) is www.OurGreenHouse.com. Pam Davis, a good friend of mine (who started out as a client), is the owner and founder of www.OurGreenHouse.com. She's a beautiful woman who functions with integrity and interest to make a difference in the world. When you buy from Pam, your money is making a difference in the bigger picture and definitely contributing to your very own child's wellbeing. (I had to put that shameless plug in!!) =)

Your Family Doctor

When you think about it, your child's body is their "living environment" and, the goal is to keep their living environment as clean and natural a possible. Continuing with this theme, you'll want to find an excellent holistic doctor that uses all-natural vitamins, herbs, medicines to help bring additional balance to their body. This is instrumental in clearing your child of an ASD!

Our first holistic doctor created a major turning point in my sons' lives. She taught me so much and helped my sons begin to clear from some of their ASD symptoms. I highly recommend finding someone in your area. Keep in mind, the more natural substances you use to restore your child's body, the easier time your child's body will have.

We use our naturopath and other holistic doctors to rebalance our sons whenever they need an "adjustment" to continue to help them evolve. We use supplements, herbs, homeopathics, etc. as a natural means to bring balance to their bodies. If they get sick, we will go to our naturopath for support. A naturopath and many other holistic doctors create healing using only natural medicines and remedies, as these medicines allow our children's cup to remain clean and empty and keeps them functioning optimally. When synthetic medicines are used consistently, their cup can actually fill up more and their ASD symptoms can become exacerbated. I'm not saying you should never use synthetic medicines, just putting the idea out there to be mindful and pick and choose what goes into your child's (and your) body with awareness and understanding.

Clean in, means clean out!

*** A little side note with some additional honesty: My family and I have been treated by several holistic doctors. All of them are great. Each helped substantially in some way. I once believed one doctor would have all our answers. I then learned through experience that no one doctor has all of anyone's answers. It's our responsibility as parents to look around and find what we need.

This is exactly what I did. It has worked beautifully for my sons (as well as for me!)

BACK TO THE BASICS

Ever notice that when your kids hang out in the house they can get bored, antsy, sometimes even argue more? This can happen especially if they're accustomed to watching television and playing video games, and suddenly those things are taken away.

What you're witnessing are children who would benefit greatly from spending time outside, and not just once in a while, but consistently, as in everyday.

I've watched this unfold with my sons. This past summer they watched some of the Summer Olympics. We limit the amount of television our sons watch, and we stretched it with the Olympics. Anyway, there were a few times when they watched a certain event during the day. I noticed when the event was over and the television was turned off, they were antsy and wanted more television. They seemed to struggle to find something else to do. It was almost as though they temporarily lost their imaginations. Everything that wasn't television seemed like a project to them.

And, to top this all off, my youngest son sat too close to the television and ended up acting a little hyper. Yes, this was all temporary, but just this little extra television viewing had an impact on them. If we allowed it everyday, it would then have a consistent impact on them. And, to be honest with you, before I knew our sons had ASDs, I was unaware of the impact of media. My oldest son watched movies at age 3 that I wouldn't let him watch now as an 11-year old. Talk about being unaware! (Or maybe just part of me not wanting to know?)

Because my husband and I weren't aware of the impact of media, we pretty much did what most people around us were doing, let our oldest son (our youngest hadn't been born yet) watch movies and play video games. Once we were exposed to the idea that media was not helpful to our child's growth and that it could have some negative implications on his behavior — ability to focus, positive mood, use of imagination, we decided to switch over.

To be quite frank, we chose to send our sons to a school that recommended no media, especially during the younger years. So, we sort of forced ourselves into this, sensing this was important to do.

Here's what we saw unfold: Both our sons learned how to sit quietly and look at books. They would spend easily an hour at our kitchen counter drawing pictures with each other. They would make up games with pillows from our couch, jump rope and play marbles. They played more actively outside whether it was raining, snowing or sunny! They started to move their bodies more, use their imaginations more and interact more cooperatively with one another! Not always cooperatively, but they were learning how to problem solve by playing with each other and sometimes arguing and then figuring out how to resolve the situation for themselves.

They started admiring what grows in our yard, taking an interest in wild-life, plants and trees. My heart has filled with love every time I think of them appreciating being in nature, noticing the world around them.

As a result of using media less and seeking other activities like spending time in nature, reading, drawing, playing backyard sports, my sons are more balanced. Being in nature has brought out their kindness. Both of my sons are more grounded and calm after spending lots of time outside.

In my mind, I often hear a specific quote from a documentary called Where Do the Children Play? I paraphrase here: "To take the wild out of the child, you must put them into the wild."

To this I say YES!

I've seen how powerful stepping away from media and replacing it with time outside can be. I'm not suggesting everyone needs to turn the television off forever. I'm just letting you know that decreasing or stepping away from media for a while can have profound effects on your child and the entire family.

Imagine if you skipped watching a daytime show or having the kids play video games one afternoon and instead you all went hiking as a family. How would that feel? From my own experience, it's very connecting, it lifts your spirits and the entire family tends to get along better after spending time together outside.

When we first starting hiking more, my kids would complain, but over time, we all came to appreciate our special time together. In the here and now it's very gratifying. Later in life, I know every member of my family will cherish all the walks we took together. I know I'm helping my sons build better feelings today by being outside more and, they're strengthening and becoming kinder more open human beings now and as they move into tomorrow.

I wish all of this for you and your kids.

EMFs

There's another form of media I want to mention. Video games, especially handheld games, computer video games, iPads, and iPhones, emit something called EMFs- electromagnetic fields. These are fields of radiation. As we're all made up of energy, the energy of our bodies and our children's bodies can be impacted by the energy emitted from these devices. As a result our body's energy can become imbalanced. Short-term result: possible headaches, moodiness, erratic behavior. Because we're seeking balance and EMFs can create an imbalance, it's healthier to limit usage of the items that emit EMFs, especially as our children are growing and the fact that we still don't know everything about the long-term effects of consistent exposure. In Europe, children under 18 are not allowed to use iPhones, smart phones, for this reason.

If you think about it, we're conducting a large experiment: What happens when humans use devices that emit radiation on a regular basis? Not sure of the results at this point, but my intuition tells me it doesn't feel right to allow my sons to use these things consistently. Not yet anyway, as their bodies are still developing.

Because we do use technology, my husband and I purchased and placed a small magnet-type item on the back of each of our computers and cell phones. The "magnet" (not really a magnet but using this word for the lack of a better term) is a neutralizer to the EMFs, possibly helping to decrease the side effects and ultimately creating a higher level of protection.

There are several of these products to choose from. We chose the Aulterra EMF Neutralizer. One of our holistic doctors recommended this brand.

TIME AT SCHOOL

Having talked about the importance of creating more natural living environments for your children, I feel it's important to point out that our children spend lots of time at school. The more natural this setting is, the more it will serve your son or daughter in balancing their ASD symptoms.

When your child attends a school that's in sync with doing things more naturally, you know your child is not only safe, but is being set up for more success in life. Since the goal is to keep cleaning out their bodies so their symptoms lessen and disappear, having a school that promotes all-natural living is helpful to this process and can accelerate healing.

My husband and I have found such a school. It's a Waldorf school. Waldorf schools are all over the U.S. and around the world. It's a school with a philosophy built on the premise that living in sync with nature, doing what's most natural for us as human beings, builds a strong foundation for our children to grow and become confident, loving, caring, responsible, compassionate, beautiful adults. And yes, highly successful adults!

There's so much more to the school's philosophy, but suffice it to say, my husband and I watch as our school and its teachers do amazing things for and with our sons everyday. This school is a blessing in both our sons' lives and our lives as their parents. Honestly, I learn from this school all of the time.

I know it's not feasible for everyone to send their child to a Waldorf school, but to even read a book on the Waldorf educational approach, to learn it for yourself, to possibly introduce some of the ideas to your child's school can make a difference in your child's life.

Something that our sons benefit from in their current school setting is how their days are structured. The Waldorf methods are based on the fact that we all follow natural rhythms. Think of how we breathe. We need to inhale and exhale to complete this action. We can't just inhale or just exhale. Either of these actions alone is not enough to live.

Activities that we engage in can be categorized as either inhale activities or exhale activities.

Here's what I mean:

When your child is learning, focusing his or her attention closely on something, this is considered an inhale activity. They're pulling in all of their energy to take in this new idea. When a child gets up, and moves his body for recess, this is an exhale activity. He can let loose!

Our children can sit at a desk (inhale) and learn for only so long before they need to exhale — get up and move around for a while.

Sitting, writing, learning= inhale
Moving around, dancing, singing= exhale

A school like a Waldorf school honors this natural rhythm and knows how crucial it is to learning and one's well-being.

Think about it, if your child could get up and move his or her body several times a day, he or she would be able to take in more information comfortably and willingly. He or she could possibly focus more easily and take interest in school and what's being taught.

This is what I see unfolding for my sons. They love a lot of what they're learning (even if my oldest son doesn't always admit it.) And, they're learning it more easily because they're doing it in an environment that supports the way their bodies naturally function.

There's so much more I could share about Waldorf schools and their amazingly beautiful approach to teaching and supporting our kids. I'm such a huge advocate for this natural way of learning (in case you haven't noticed!)

How Does Your House Make You Feel?

When my house has been cluttered and messy, I have physically felt cluttered and messy. I noticed my family and I arguing more, each of us seeming less focused and more confused.

When I have argued with my husband, I have then found myself subconsciously standing beside my dresser drawer, cleaning out old clothes, or going through a pile of papers on the kitchen counter.

What's going on when this happens? Something in me is directing me to clean things up. When we get rid of clutter and clean up our living spaces, we as a family all begin to feel better. We think better. We act better. There's a different energy in your house when it's clean and organized versus messy and cluttered.

What's Displayed in Your Home?

Take a closer look around your house. Aside from how organized it is, what items have you chosen to surround yourself with? Do you have lots of photos of family and friends? Beautiful uplifting paintings? Do the colors in each of the rooms create a sense of calm or do they have you feeling bored and drab?

We once had a painting of a sailboat with its mast down, sitting in a harbor, hanging on our staircase wall. The boat and the harbor were painted shades of grey. The painting depicted a cold, rainy day. I realized one day,

after learning the power and impact of what we chose to surround ourselves with, that this painting elicited a feeling of sadness and loneliness.
And, it was a giant painting! At this point in time, my family and I had
been feeling lots of sadness and loneliness. So I enlisted my husband to
take it down.

I replaced it with a map of the world.

Since the painting was removed, there has been a greater flow of happiness
and feeling more connected as a family.

Funny thing, my oldest son Forrest has also been asking about traveling around the world, "When can we travel around the world mom?" I
wouldn't be surprised if several opportunities began to present themselves!
=)

My suggestion to you: Look around your home. How do all of your knick-
knacks and photographs, etc., make you feel? Good, keep them. Bad, shift
them out. You want you and your family to feel good in your home. Good
energy in the home allows all of you to relax, feel comfortable and re-
charge. We *need* our homes to feel like a beautiful safe haven that we look
forward to spending time in. Our kids function much better when this is
the case. And, of course, we get to feel wonderful too!

RESTORE KEY O

"OM", LISTEN TO YOUR INTUITION

BODEN'S SIX-MONTH DOCTOR'S VISIT

When I went to the pediatrician for my youngest son Boden's six-month inoculations, something in me was questioning if they were all necessary. I had always followed what the pediatrician had recommended. I wanted to be a "good mother" and keep my sons healthy. For some reason, this particular time around, something in me was questioning if it was necessary. It was more of a feeling than a concrete idea or fact.

As it turns out, this was the series of vaccinations that strongly impacted my youngest son's body. His cup was filling up (unbeknownst to us) and this series of vaccinations caused his cup to spill over. Two weeks after these vaccinations, Boden began to shake and roll his eyeballs to the back of his head and lost all of his motor coordination. Boden soon thereafter showed signs of autism.

Fast-forward several years — Boden is healed.

How did we get here? Well, I recognized that one of the things that allowed autism into Boden's life was not listening to my intuition. And, it just so happened that what helped to restore his body (and both of my sons' bodies) was learning to listen to my intuition.

When I sat in that pediatrician's office and had a feeling that maybe I shouldn't give all of those vaccinations to my son, I didn't follow that feeling. I overrode the feeling with the assurances from the nurse and doctor that the vaccinations were safe. I allowed their knowledge to trump my inner knowing.

At that time, I had no clue that I had something called intuition and that it existed to guide me to what was right for me.

Had I known about intuition and listened to the clear feeling it was giving me, I would not be writing this book.

It's okay. There's no blame of doctors, nurses or me for that matter. We can all only follow what we know. Doctors couldn't have predicted what would happen to Boden; as far as they know most children are fine with vaccinations. I didn't know from a factual standpoint that vaccinations or other products could be unhealthy for infants. It was a learning experience for me.

You can consult with doctors, psychologists, and any other expert you can imagine. They are all very important people, and it is good to hear what they have to say, but you need to go with what feels right! You need to let your body tell you what's best, not what someone else's statistics show as your probable future.

I stopped solely listening to doctors and therapists and began to listen to the feeling inside of me that said, "They're only giving you a part of what your sons need. There's more Andrea, keep looking."

Or, "No, what they just told you is not true for you. Your sons are moving past these symptoms. This is just a temporary stop on the ladder to complete healing."

Or, "I can't possibly do what they're suggesting. It feels wrong!"

Intuition has all of your answers. All of them.

What Exactly Is Intuition?

Intuition is that part of us that's not tangible. Just like an idea is intangible until it's put into action and a product or thing is created as a result. Intuition is intangible. It can show up as a thought, idea, it can come to you in words, pictures or just a feeling.

Intuition is often felt in the "gut" area of your body. It's that uncomfortable feeling in your stomach when something is off or it's that excited uplifted, light feeling you get when something is so right!

Intuition speaks to you in the form of feelings, and, when you really learn how to listen to intuition, it can speak to you through words, or images.

When you hear about people meditating to find their answers, they're basically connecting with their intuition to hear what's best for them.

In the past, I didn't pay much attention to my intuition. Not until something broke in my life. Having my kids land on the spectrum felt like something broke in my life. In the midst of trying to figure out next steps to supplement all of the other holistic things I was already doing for my sons, I read *The Self Healing Cookbook,* by Kristina Turner.

In this book, Kristina introduces you to an approach to better understand what's happening to your body and gain insights on how to help yourself, in other words, hear your intuition more clearly. One particular exercise guides you to lie down, relax your breathing for a few minutes and count backwards slowly while breathing calmly. Once you count backwards from 10, you ask yourself aloud, what can I do to help myself?

Well, I tried it and it *worked*! I had never tried it before (minus one time in college) and wow, I was amazed at the answer to my question that floated through my mind. It was an answer that I would have NEVER come up with on my own. This answer felt so good. I was giddy with excitement, first, because I actually heard my intuition speak to me and second, because I loved what was being suggested — it felt right.

I now regularly listen to my intuition. I meditate 5 to 10 minutes most days. Yup, that's it, just 5 to 10 minutes. I try to keep it simple and completely manageable.

I know that if I can do this, you can do this too. It's simpler than you might think. I encourage you to give it a try!

When you learn to tune into your intuition you get to hear what's best for you and your family. You get to bypass deliberating and worrying if you're doing the right thing.

Imagine going to a doctor or some other expert and immediately knowing if the recommendations they're giving feels right. You begin to save yourself a whole lot of time and energy because you don't have to follow everything you're told, only the things that feel right.

When you learn to hear what you're intuition is saying, your life gets easier. Instead of feeling like a fish swimming upstream, you now shift direction and go with the flow. Your child still may be involved in different activities to support his or her healing, only now, there's only one or two you pursue, because your intuition eliminated the therapies that were not so important.

By listening to your intuition, you slow down more, have less things to fit into your schedule for your kids. Your intuition showed you what to cut out and too many extracurricular activities was a big one. You realized that the idea that too many activities were a drain on your child and that thought wasn't a passing thought, it was actually your intuition kicking in and trying to guide you and your children to what was better for you.

Follow your intuition; it will lead you to an easier, happier life. A life where your child is quite possibly cleared of ASD symptoms!

Following my intuition has helped me to take steps with my sons' healing that I would have never previously pursued when I didn't know how to follow my intuition. The steps my intuition led me to are the 7 RESTORE Keys I share in this book. I would never in a million years have done all of these things had it not been for my willingness to follow what felt right versus what I thought I should do.

Be BOLD. Learn to follow your own inner voice, your intuition. Intuition **Heals**.

How to Hear Your Intuition

There are many ways to hear the messages your intuition is trying to convey.

The easiest way is to pay attention to what feels good and what doesn't.

When you do something or follow advice that feels good, you are following your intuition.

When you do something and you feel frustrated, resentful or just somehow not good about what you're up to, you are not following your intuition. You're going against it.

Feel good= following intuition
Feel bad= not following your intuition

When doctors were trying to uncover what was happening to Boden — why was he shaking his head rapidly and rolling his eyeballs to the back of his head, why had he lost his motor coordination? — the neurologist, after running a brain scan on Boden said the tests came back fine. I knew in my gut that wasn't the case. He may have been free of seizures, but something else was going on.

Listening to the neurologist's report stating Boden was okay had me feeling uncomfortable and somewhat frustrated. Shortly thereafter, once I researched and found our first holistic doctor, I felt elated. I felt excited. I just knew we were onto something big for them. I was (without knowing) following my intuition and what was right for my sons.

ADDITIONAL WAYS TO HEAR YOUR INTUITION

I learned along the way that there are several ways you can tune in to what your intuition is saying.

Going with how you feel regarding a situation is the easiest and most obvious way, but sometimes we're looking for more information. Like what is the best school for my child? Or, what is the next best step to help my child do really well in school? We sense there's more that can be done, we're just not sure off the top of our heads where to go to help our kids or to help ourselves.

This is when learning additional ways of hearing the messages your intuition is trying to relay can really come in handy.

When you learn how to do this, you'll be able to ask a question and then "hear" your answer. Sometimes the answer comes immediately, sometimes it takes a day or two. You put the question out there and then you relax and trust that the answer will come.

Here are some of the ways I've been able to connect with my intuition and hear its important messages:

Slowing down- You hear it time and again. Slowing down is the first major step toward hearing your intuition speak. If you remain in a busy or stressed state, you will not be able to hear what's important for you and your family. When you slow down, ideas and thoughts come to you. Keep in mind, these thoughts and ideas tend to be messages from your intuition, especially if they excite you when you think about them!

Journal- If you sit down with your journal, with the intention of hearing the answer to an important question, you will be amazed at what ideas come through as you write. Start with asking your question aloud. Specifically ask your intuition to answer your question on the pages of your journal. Next, sit quietly, close your eyes and wait a minute or two before you begin writing.

At first it may feel like it's the ideas in your brain that you're writing down. As you continue writing, you'll notice that the ideas that are being written are not ideas you would have come up with on your own.

This is intuition speaking. I've written in a journal quite a bit. I remember one time asking what do to about an argument my husband and I were having. What came to me through journaling was not anything I would have chosen to do, not yet anyway. I was dead set on waiting for my husband to apologize. My intuition clearly told me to be the first to reach out and make things better, that it needed to be me. Not what I wanted to hear, but I knew in an instant this was the TRUTH. When I chose to follow it, things felt better. If I chose to ignore it, I would have unnecessarily made things more difficult for myself.

I've since learned I like my life being easy. So, I follow my intuition all of the time now!

Other ways to hear your intuition: meditation, yoga, going for a quiet walk, just sitting quietly, painting and dancing.

When you do something that you love, something that involves minimal thinking, allows you to slow down, relax, and feel comfortable, you're setting yourself up to hear your intuition and its powerful messages.

I recall one time wanting to find the answer to a question. After awhile, I pretty much forgot I was questioning something. I moved about my days without a thought of the question I had. An evening or two later, I decided to dance in my living room — something my family is now very accustomed to watching me do. As I moved my body to the music, spontaneous ideas began to pop into my head. Each of these ideas excited me. Without realizing it or even trying, I connected with my intuition while dancing and was given the answers I was looking for. How cool is that?

If you decide you'd like to try connecting with your intuition, remember you'll want to start with asking your important question. Ask your question out loud — it's more powerful that way and your intuition is then more clear about what it is you want to know.

When you choose to have fun you are making yourself a conduit for more clearly hearing what your intuition wants you to know. Seek pleasure in all that you do. This doesn't mean you run around skipping your responsibilities and just have a good time. It means you remain responsible but you choose to engage in activities and events that feel less like obligations and reflect more of what you really enjoy doing. Doing what feels good opens you up for more good and for hearing what's most important for your family.

Funny thing- having fun and enjoying yourself is what's most important. Bet your intuition will tell you this!

Remember hearing and following your intuition is a powerful tool to help you more easily clear your child's ASD symptoms. And, its use goes well beyond that. If you follow your intuition's messages diligently you will meet with the most amazing life you ever thought possible! I smile as I write this, because I feel so blessed — this is exactly what's unfolding for me, and I wish this for you too!

RESTORE KEY R

RESPECT AND APPRECIATE YOURSELF

WHY IS IT IMPORTANT TO RESPECT AND APPRECIATE YOURSELF?

When I began healing my kids, I felt like I gave my all to the process. I was a busy bee, with the sole purpose of making life better for my kids, making sure they felt good and had a great life now and in the future. If one of our holistic doctors recommended we do something, even if I was already doing 20 other things, I did it! When therapies were recommended, I happily obliged. (this was pre check-with-my-intuition days!) I was going to do everything in my power to make sure my sons were okay.

As a result of all this giving of myself to my sons, they started to heal — a wonderful event that honestly kept me motivated, though my health started to decline. Food and environmental allergies appeared, digestive concerns, emotional stuff surfaced. What the heck was going on? Things were supposed to be getting better in our lives; I wasn't ready to focus on fixing anything else.

What was really happening was that my body was responding to not being respected or appreciated. If you give your all to someone else or something else — even if it's a noble cause like healing your kids — you will burn out as I did. Your body will try to get your attention through weight gain, or too much weight loss. You will feel more emotional and act more extreme. Or you might just feel tired, depressed and uninterested in much other than helping your kids. You lose your vigor and vitality.

Through the process of giving so much of myself, I never stopped to give myself attention. My sole focus on my kids felt extremely important to follow, and at the time was the only thing I could imagine doing. Yet it wasn't the best thing to do. Placing all of my emphasis on my sons was a way of *disrespecting me.*

I didn't understand what was happening for sometime. I kept up with this same approach and continued to give my kids my all, meanwhile squeezing in vitamins and herbs for me to help bring balance to my body, but never going beyond to do anything else for myself.

Over time, my kids plateaued. Their bodies had cleared significantly, but seemed to get stuck. It was almost like that was the highest level of healing they could reach. It wasn't; it just seemed like it at the time.

It was somewhere around this time that I began to understand if I wanted my life and my kids to get better, I needed to start to respect myself more. To love myself.

Giving to my kids was indeed important and powerful, but I realized I didn't need to give all of me. I needed to give some of me, and to learn to give to myself as well. I, my kids, and my whole family would benefit when I decided to give to myself.

This is exactly what happened. I slowly and very uncomfortably started to exercise more, connect with Spirit in the morning, occasionally go out with friends and attend self-development events. Each of these activities began to add to my self-love basket. I was starting to take care of myself. I became stronger, exercised more healthy boundaries with my kids (I learned how to say "no thank you" more) and gained more respect for doing so.

As I began to feel better, I learned to imagine more for my family and I, instead of seeing us as stuck! This more open and positive mindset then allowed me to attract different circumstances in my life. When I felt better, I could more easily stay open-minded to the possibility of my sons healing entirely. With this thought in mind, things began to improve for both of my sons.

And when mom feels good, there's an energy that affects everyone in the family, and this level of good energy supports everyone feeling better! It just does.

And it's only natural that when mom feels good the potential to heal her children goes up exponentially!

I want to make sure I'm being very clear, because I know how hard it was for me to grasp and accept that I needed to make myself a priority. I sense that it might be just as difficult for you too. If so, that's perfectly under-standable.

As you grow more open to the idea that **YOU are important and giving to yourself is an expression of self-respect and appreciation, I invite you to take steps to help yourself, to show yourself lots of love.** Your kids need you to do this, more than you may know. And your beautiful body needs you to do this, more than you may know.

This RESTORE Key goes *deep*. When you really get into helping yourself you'll begin to touch places within yourself you've never touched before. **You'll begin to heal from the inside out and your children will mirror this process!**

This RESTORE Key may sound a lot like the HELP Heal Mindset I recom-mend. It is. It reiterates the "P" in the HELP Heal Mindset, which rep-resents Prioritize you.

Because I'm intimately familiar with how difficult it can be for a woman to step out of the Supermom Mindset and really allow herself to be a priority in her life, I thought it important to have a Key that not only **reinforces** the importance of this, but does something **MORE**.

This Key represents going deeper. Not just making time for yourself, which is an awesome accomplishment, but it represents finding ways to see why you haven't made time for you, seeing what's really been getting in your way.

More importantly, this key shows you how to move past placing yourself last on your list, so that you can make life better for you and your child.

When you put this Key into practice, you begin to see the false thoughts and ideas that have gotten in your way and allowed you to sadly disrespect yourself and neglect appreciating you.

Do any of the following thoughts seem familiar?

"I need to help my kids first, then I'll see if I have time."
"It's selfish to take care of me."
"I don't matter enough to take care of me."
"I have to fix this or no one else will."
"Everyone else has a great life, except me."
"I'm not as attractive, smart, confident or as good of a mother as they are."
"They are an awesome parent. Look at how kind and understanding they are- they probably never yell."
"Poor me, this is all I get — a child on the spectrum and a house in chaos."
"I don't really deserve any better."
"Wish I could be as good as them."
"If I show up as me, no one will like me."

You didn't get to this space by accident. You got here because of how you feel about yourself deep down, possibly on a subconscious level. If you choose, you can unravel these limiting thoughts. Let go of them. Make peace with them. See them for what they really are — false.

These thoughts, and I venture to guess many more, have been ruling your life and have helped you to create the life you have now.

If you want better, if you want more for your child and your whole family, you'll want to start learning how to respect and appreciate yourself.

MY OWN STORY

I came to a crossroads in healing my sons. I noticed that my sons were doing pretty well overall, at school they acted fine, got along with others well and they were comfortable and kind to friends. But when we were home alone my husband and I would still have difficulty with them. There would be arguing, yelling, grasping at any new discipline technique that sounded even remotely decent to try. Let's just say things were still very chaotic at home.

One day I went for a non-relaxing jog in which I replayed over and over in my mind an argument my husband and I had over our kids and their behavior. In the midst of a crying fit, as I slowed my pace and neared my home, the thought came to me — I needed to do something else. I realized loud and clear that I had helped heal my sons immensely, but because chaos was still prevalent in our home, I needed to do more. I needed to heal me.

This was not just about them any longer. It was about me.

It **HAD** to be about me too, or we'd stay stuck!

I needed to figure out how to stop the behind-closed-doors family chaos. I wanted to feel good, really good, and I thought with all that I accomplished I would have felt great by now. But, I didn't.

This is when I first learned about Louise Hay, an amazing spiritual leader and self love guru. I read one of her books, listened to several CDs of her lectures and began working with a coach to make peace with my limiting thoughts, the exact thoughts that were perpetually allowing me to disrespect myself and create a lonely, unfulfilling life.

Fast-forward a few years. I've made peace with many of those limiting thoughts. I won't kid you, I'm not perfectly over every limiting thought I ever had, but I'm feeling great! I'm stronger and much more confident. I respect myself a whole lot more than ever before.

Learning to respect and appreciate myself has helped my life to look different.

My kids show me more love and interest. They really enjoy (most of the time) when I drop them off at school and give them a hug and kiss, I can feel an energy and see a look in their eyes that says, "Yes, thank you."

My oldest son didn't always liked to be touched, so this is a beautiful thing!

When my sons ask if they can go over a friend's house after school and I know it would throw off our dinner, homework and getting ready for bed routine, I'm more inclined to say, "no thanks." Before, I'd want my kids to be happy and I would decide it was fine to go with the flow. As I'm practicing healthy boundaries, my kids are learning healthy boundaries.

Guess what? As a result, Forrest comes home from school and typically is the one to initiate starting his homework. He looks at the clock and says – "Four o'clock, time to get started."

Considering I used to have to ask for something 25 times before it happened, this is a major upgrade!

These are just minute examples of how love and respect have raised my life to another level, with my sons' healing well surpassing that ceiling.

I've noticed as I appreciate and respect myself, my family and other people have started to respect me more. People can feel the energy of someone who stands with confidence and gracefully speaks her mind. When we love ourselves, we attract more love from others.

Making peace with limiting thoughts helped me to open up to loving myself more. Loving myself more helped me to feel more love, and give more love to everyone in my life.

My sons have felt this love and respect and have grown to show me and others more love because of it.

Love is more healing than any vitamin, herb or medicine out there. Love you and watch the most amazing things happen in your life, to your kids, and you!

FEELING GOOD ENOUGH

Time for me to be straight with you. I learned something significant on my journey to heal my sons. I learned that anyone who has a child with ADD, ADHD, autism or any ASD has this inner feeling that they're not good enough.

This inner feeling, very often subconscious, drives them to do everything in their power to please others, to try to be perfect so they won't be judged — to do what others are doing so they can fit in.

As I mentioned in the HELP Heal Mindset- E- Everything Happens for a Reason. You didn't end up with a child on the spectrum by accident. He or she is here for you to learn that you are good enough. That you don't need to fit in. They're here to show you need to love and respect yourself so that things in your current life can heal.

When you have a child on the spectrum, what happens? You all stand out more. As a mother, you are judged if your child acts up. People automatically think, what's her problem? And they sometimes turn away in distaste.

I went through this. I know you have too. My reaction was to cry. I felt so unfairly misjudged.

When my son would hit others, I felt so upset for the other child, I was sad for my son, who was looked upon as bad and, honestly, I felt sorry for me, for having people think I was a bad mother. Who the heck raises a son that hits?

It took some time, but when I began to look at this situation differently, I could see myself responding to being judged. I knew as this happened time and again; there was a message in this feeling.

This concern for what others thought was too powerful for me to ignore.

I explored it.

Then it came to me. What if I didn't care what others thought? What if I stopped caring what others think? If I stopped caring so much then I wouldn't get hurt every time someone judged my kids and I.

I pondered how could I execute this. What could help me to let go of what others think?

What came to me was what I learned in Louise Hay's book, *You Can Heal Your Life*. I learned if I **love** myself I won't be so concerned with what others think.

Lack of loving myself is what got me in the place of being so needy of others' approval. Loving myself would strengthen me from the inside out and allow me to notice what others think of me, be understanding to them, but be strong and remember the truth in the moments of being judged. My family and I are absolutely wonderful people, regardless of what anyone else thinks.

By strengthening my love for myself, I began needing others' approval less.

By strengthening my love for myself, I watched as my sons grew stronger and stronger and began to heal even further.

RESPECTING AND LOVING MYSELF HELPED HEAL MY SONS

How did my sons grow stronger and continue to heal just from me learning to love myself?

Remember the Universal Law? What you think, you attract into your life.

Well, if you have subconscious thoughts that you are not good enough, you manifest situations that have you feeling not good enough. Like energy attracts like energy.

If your kid's behaviors, actions, inability to do certain things has you feeling like your child isn't up to par with other kids, and has you embarrassed at the thought of what other parents/teachers might think of them or you. BOOM, there it is.

Your subconscious thought of not feeling good enough brings you circumstances (like your child's ASD) to be judged, and in turn leaves you feeling "not good enough." You can only manifest in your life what you feel and think.

By learning to love and respect yourself, you begin to attract less judgment -and more understanding and support from others.

By learning to love and respect yourself you begin to heal YOU from the inside out. Your children will start to mirror this.

When I stopped being concerned with what others thought, it was because I was thinking, I am good enough. I am a good person regardless of what they think. So, if Forrest or Boden did something that someone else judged as negative, instead of FOCUSING on what I thought my sons did wrong, I let it go. I gave it little to no energy.

And, when I stopped focusing on what I thought someone else perceived they did wrong, it gave me the opportunity to see what they were doing that was right! I got to see and appreciate all the things they were doing that were wonderful!

See, I was so stuck in reacting to being judged by others and then honestly, in turn, judging my kids for that, that I was missing a big part of the important picture.

My kids weren't wrong. They were wonderful, and were doing lots and lots of things right. But I had to stop focusing on the negative in order to see what was really positive all along.

I had to stop focusing on negative, if I wanted to stop having negative in my life.

I'd like to make this clear; the flow goes something like this:

I love myself more = less concern for outside judgment = bypassing judging my sons = noticing the good in my sons= more good things happening to my sons = my sons healing.

So, the deal is, you won't heal your kids if you listen to outside judgment and judge your kids and yourself accordingly.

You HEAL yourself and your kids when you rise above this.

You rise above this when you love yourself.

How to Start the Process of LOVING YOU

I didn't just do one thing and voilà, I was healed and lovin' myself up and down, day in day out! Oh no. It was more involved than that.

I began a process of consistently practicing ways to clear out the old limiting thoughts and put in the new, more loving thoughts.

Following are some of the practices that I used (and still use), and of course there are always a million more ways to practice loving yourself, do what feels best.

I do recommend that you pick a least two of the following and create a routine for yourself. These practices have the biggest impact on shifting your thinking and upgrading your family and your life when you follow them EVERYDAY. If an approach gets old or boring, switch it. Make sure what you're doing feels good. Trust your intuition to guide you to what's best.

SELF LOVE EXERCISES

5 Minutes of Gratitude - Start your day and end your day thinking of what you're grateful for. When you focus on what feels good, and it could be anything by the way, your bed, the color of your pjs, the book you're reading, the wonderful early time you went to bed last night...on and on... You shift your energy from worry and negativity to love and happiness. When you feel happier, it's much easier to see the good in yourself (and your kids)!

I practice this one everyday. It's easy and REALLY powerful!!!

Mirror - Hold up a mirror, look at yourself and say, "I love you" to your reflected image. Watch what happens. I've had clients do this same thing and very often the response is, "Do I have to do this, can we skip it?" Or tears. Lots and lots of tears. Many women don't like themselves. Looking at themselves closely they see only flaws, not beautifulness. It's time to change that. Your kids need you to change that. More importantly, you need you to change that.

Begin with looking at yourself in a mirror everyday and saying, "I love you." Or asking, "What would it feel like to love you?" If only anger, or sadness comes up when you say I love you, that's good, it's just old buried emotions surfacing and needing to come out. Stand in front of the mirror and ask yourself the question of what it would feel like to love yourself, do this at least ten times in a row. Do this every chance you get. If it helps, make it a practice to ask this at least five times a day. In the beginning the more you ask this the more you'll start to feel a difference in yourself.

This exercise, as all the exercises will do, will help you to see where you were stuck, and help you to move into what you're really meant to feel — love for yourself.

I would do this exercise in the rear view mirror of my car. I'd angle the mirror down so I could see myself and I'd sit there talking to myself, repeating my question over and over. "What would it feel like to love you?" I tried not to do this while driving, though I admit, I did so a few times. I would usually sit in parking lots and do this before I got out of my car. Anyone walking by probably thought I was a little nutty. Oh well! That's the power of loving yourself more; you just don't mind what they think.

Watch What You Say - Universal Law tells us: What you think and feel you create. This goes for the words you speak too.

If you want to have a healthy happy life and feel good about yourself and your children, and of course help your children clear from ASDs, begin to pay attention to the words you choose to use when you describe yourself or your family. Notice yourself and try to stop yourself from saying negative things.

I noticed I was inadvertently making fun of my kids and myself. Why? I did it so as not to be judged by others — to beat them to the punch.

I put a halt to this nonsense. I knew if I wanted my family and I to continue to improve I had to say only loving things about us. That's it. Every time I complained about my kids, what they did or didn't do, or anytime I put myself down to make someone else look good, I was putting out to the

Universe energy and thoughts that my family and I weren't good enough. I decided it was time to move past being stuck.

Paying attention to your words can have a big impact on clearing ASDs and upgrading your family's life.

It's interesting when you start to pay attention to the words you use and how you talk about yourself to others. This can be an eye opener. Do you commiserate with other parents about the woes of your children and how others treat them, or do you complain to your spouse about how difficult Johnny was today? Do you constantly vent to your friend about your son's teacher not being sensitive enough to his needs?

You'll want to nip all this talk in the bud if you want to go FURTHER.

It may feel awkward at first. You may be accustomed to speaking this way. Most people are, it's a habit. Your grandparents, parents, teachers, the media, they've all spoken to you this way for most of your life. Nobody was wrong for doing this, they didn't know any better.

But now, you do. If you want better for your family, you'll want to practice choosing your words wisely. Talk about what you want, not what you don't want. Say nice things about yourself. This may be difficult, that's okay. All new habits take practice, and saying only nice things about yourself is a new practice for most people.

Go back to your journal where you began to practice RESTORE Key R-Rewrite Reality. Reread what you wrote for your IDEAL reality. Start using words that support living THAT life!

Ooh baby! When you do this, the Universe is sure to bring you the good stuff!

Speak Up for What You Want - Or, as John Mayer so eloquently puts it, "Say what you need to say!"

Saying what you REALLY want to say is an act of love for yourself.

I shared with you in the "H" of the HELP Heal Mindset the importance of honoring your feelings and saying what you feel, instead of burying your feelings. I'm repeating this because I want to strongly reinforce the importance of practicing to ask for what you want. Also, standing up for yourself if you feel uncomfortable with something and honestly sharing what's on your mind. Lots and lots of women don't want to rock the boat, they want everyone to be happy. They never really make a choice of what they want, they let friends, their family, acquaintances make their choices: "Where do you want to go to eat? I don't know, where do you want to go to eat…?" "What do you want to do tonight? I don't know what do you want to do?"

Or, you're not happy with what's happening at school, you think some of your child's teachers could do a better job. You don't say anything, instead you chalk it up to, is it really a big deal? You let it go, you really don't want any of the teachers to feel bad, after all, you like them, you really just don't like some of what they're doing. You minimize the situation to make it easier to let go of it, and then you never have to say what you were really feeling.

Asking for what you want and saying what you feel may feel difficult at first: patterns have been ingrained. Start small. When ordering food at a restaurant, don't just eat what the waiter brings you if it's not to your liking. Return it. You can still be kind and polite in your request to switch it to what you really want.

At the grocery store, if you want your groceries packed in the bags a certain way — cold stuff with cold, dried with dried — ask for it. Find ways that feel smaller and more doable to practice asking for what you want. Build up your speaking-up-for-yourself muscle.

I had a heck of a time with this one. I allowed myself to be a "go with the flow" sort of person. When you do what everyone else wants to do, you bypass conflict, everyone likes you. When I first starting speaking up it seemed out of character. I think most people didn't take me seriously. I didn't even take me seriously. It felt nerve-wracking to say what I really wanted.

So, I retreated for a while, went back to blending in, it was much easier. But, with trouble brewing on the home front — arguments and chaos — I knew I had to start to speak up if I wanted to clear the mess and make things better, for all of us.

I began speaking up for myself. My kids and husband did not like it. I met with lots of resistance. Over time, they started to see the importance and wisdom in what I was saying. And, when they didn't, I learned to not care so much if they understood; it was a matter of living in alignment with what I felt. I had to do it for me, knowing full well there would be a huge ripple effect that would support them.

Say what you need to say, girlfriends. Keep practicin'!

Visualize - Pick certain days of the week and incorporate visualizing into your regular routine. Think of the negative thoughts you have about yourself, or anyone in your life. Imagine them as images. It could be an image of a monster, a giant blob, sheep, lightening bolts, whatever your mind can imagine. Watch these images as they leave your body and drift out into the Universe, far, far away.

Dr Bernie Segel, a well known holistic cancer doctor, prior to his retirement, facilitated support groups in which he helped patients to visualize the cancer leaving their bodies. Those that were able to do this consistently had a greater chance at recovering. Why? Because visualizing is a technique that helps the body let go of old stagnant energy and releasing stagnant energy helps to heal. Ideas, thoughts, you can let them all go if you choose.

Letting these old stagnant limiting thoughts go frees up space in your mind and your heart for more love. Love for YOU that is!

If you'd like, make a list of the limiting thoughts you've noticed yourself having. Go back to this list often. You can then go through the list one by one and watch your limiting thoughts travel off out into the abyss.

A special request: When you follow this visualizing practice, as you watch your limiting thought leave your body and travel outward, let it know what you appreciate about it, how it helped you, because it has. That thought has helped you grow somehow. It's added value to your life, you don't want to send it off in distaste: "Get the heck out of here." Instead, give it appreciation and love. Thank it.

Make Peace with Limiting Thoughts - Two words for you: Byron Katie. Bryon Katie is an amazing woman, speaker, author and spiritual leader who helps people turn their negative thoughts around and see the TRUTH. She has a system called The Work. It consists of a few questions, it's so simple and yet so powerful.

I use The Work consistently. It helps me to get out of my own way. When something comes up for me, a disagreement with someone, I know it's time for me to do The Work. I go for a jog and go through the questions out loud. Usually by the time I return home, I've turned my negative thought into a more peaceful thought. This stuff is powerful. I recommend it to anyone. Visit ByronKatie.com, print off the four questions and begin using them when you feel stuck.

Forgiveness - If you want to feel better about yourself, let go of old grudges. And, just like with visualizing, it will clear space in your heart for more love.

We can't love ourselves fully if we're judging and holding things against others. Our judgment of others is really just a displacement of our judgment toward ourselves. Stop judging others as wrong and you'll begin to see yourself with more softness and love.

Make a list of those toward which you harbor any ill feelings. One by one, think about how you may have contributed to the situation in some way. We always do, it's never a one-way street.

Write a letter to them. You never have to send it (unless you want to). It's for therapeutic purposes. Or, journal what you're forgiving. You can visualize the person you've been upset with. Imagine having a conversation with them. Give them your love and understanding. Do this for everyone on your list.

Man, this stuff is liberating and freeing! There's nothing like loving others more. This feeling is powerful and hugely wonderful for you and your family!

Welcome Support - Trying to do all of these exercises can be daunting when you already have a family and at least one child with an ASD. I get it. Do what I did. Hire a coach. Chances are you will get farther much faster if you're held accountable and you have someone cheering you on consistently. A good coach can see more clearly where you're stuck and can offer advice relevant to you, as to how to move past it.

Enlist even more support. Reach out to your spouse or a few close friends. Tell them what you're up to. The more you allow yourself to be supported, the easier it will be to step out of those old limiting thoughts and begin lovin' yourself!

Negative Self Thoughts Fill Up Your Cup

Remember in Section One when I shared with you the empty cup theory?

Negative thoughts about yourself are toxic to your body. They will fill up your cup just as easily as outside chemicals do.

If you think consciously or subconsciously that you need to be perfect, you can't show up less than perfect. You might think the following:

- You have to fit in
- All other moms know what they're doing and you're the only screw up
- Everyone else has it easier than you

Any of these self-defeating thoughts are negative, and, when consistently thought and believed, will fill your cup with more toxins.

You are better than those thoughts; you need your cup to be clean so you can feel awesome about yourself. So you can be more present as a mom. So you can bust that glass ceiling on clearing ASDs once and for all!

Amen sista'! Keep those respectful lovin' thoughts goin' about yourself- I'm pluggin' for ya!!

RESTORE KEY E

ESTABLISH BALANCE IN KEY AREAS OF LIFE

WHAT'S THE PURPOSE OF ESTABLISHING BALANCE IN KEY AREAS OF YOUR LIFE?

When your life is more balanced, you *feel* much better.

If you have a career you love, something that motivates you in the morning to get ready for the day, something you look forward to, this adds value to you and you can feel terrific as a result.

If you and your spouse or significant other get along really well, you fully support each other, you see the best in one another, this allows you to shine brighter, to be your best, to share your best with the world.

If you have a cool work/life schedule, lots of free time, fun time and time for dates with your spouse, time with yourself, you feel phenomenal!

When you have a spiritual practice, it doesn't matter what the heck you practice, just the act of connecting with something more, something bigger, you feel supported and more grounded and tapping into those loving feelings becomes easy.

Think of the last time you had a day off from work or a fun day with friends. How did you feel? Good chance you felt really invigorated.

How about a special time you and your spouse had a terrific day together. You laughed, held hands and spent time talking and connecting. Once again, you probably felt glad to be alive.

This is what having balance in key areas of life can do for you.

As you establish balance in key areas of your life: **Health, Career, Relationship, Spirituality, Movement, Finances, Fun, Contribution**, you feel more vibrant then ever!

What do you think happens to children of parents who feel vibrant? They begin to feel more vibrant too! There is an energy to feeling good — it's hugely and wonderfully contagious!

When you feel good, your kids can clear through their symptoms more easily. You're like a rock star on stage, getting everyone watching you to clap and dance. You lead that room with your energy. You lead your kids with that energy too!

Spending time creating balance in these areas can really accelerate healing for your kids.

HEALTH

It goes without saying, if your body is healthy and balanced, your moods, your actions and reactions tend to be more balanced, calmer, kinder and more in alignment with what serves you and your family best. If your health is off, find a holistic doctor or health coach and begin taking small steps to strengthen your health.

CAREER

When you have a career you love being involved with, you have more positive energy to share with everyone, your kids included.

If your current career feels stagnant or you don't like what you're up to, take steps to improve your current working situation. Can you shift your work schedule? Can you take on a new project? Can you spend time with more positive people while at work? Small shifts can have a big impact on your interest in your work.

If your current career doesn't feel right, take steps to shift careers. When I was working temporarily for a non-profit organization, I enjoyed the people and many components of the job, but it wasn't my dream career. I knew my heart wanted something different. So, while I was still at that job, I began to write this book. I started doing something that felt exciting. Something I felt passionate about and looked forward to being a part of. This kept the wind in my sails!

You decide what feels best. Nobody else but you creates your life, so go for it!

RELATIONSHIP

There are two important areas of focus: **Spousal/ significant other** relationship and **parent/child relationship.**

Spousal/Significant other- How is this relationship? Do you get along well with your spouse or significant other? Do you have a loving relationship built on trust? Do you look forward to being together? If not, you'll want to get clear, is this relationship for you or not? If it is and it's feeling off, make time for therapy or coaching. You need to feel good about your key relationships. They are either big energy drainers or big energy enhancers.

Figure out what you need to feel good. Share with your spouse. If you're both interested in making things work, go for it! Your goal is to not only get along well, but to bring excitement and happiness back into your life.

Additionally, it is important to share that having kids, especially kids with any type of ASD, you and your spouse want to be on the same page with parenting. If you aren't, many arguments will arise. The kids get confused and then they begin to take sides. The arguing itself creates a level of fear. The kids feel ungrounded. This can be a breeding ground for their lack of self-esteem.

On the flip side, when you and your spouse get along and support each other, your children feel the power of your messages. They have an easier time listening. They see you and your spouse as a beautiful united front that's looking out for their best. Not two resentful people picking fights. They learn this stuff from observing; it all goes in!

Child Parent Relationship- How do you and your children get along? Do you feel close? Do you share your real feelings easily with one another? Do you both feel supported and understood by each other? Do you share lots of playful loving moments that touch your heart?

Or, do you find yourself getting caught up in what your kids have done "wrong," Johnny left his socks on the floor again! Susie is always leaving her toys around the house. Jake is constantly making fun of his brother. Justin won't sit still for dinner.

If you find yourself focusing often on what your children have done wrong, you are not alone. All parents have done this to some degree. It's a sign that your relationship with them would be served best with a tune up!

What's a tune up? A realignment of your parenting approach.

Kids don't like to be yelled at and told what to do all of the time. How do I know? Simply because I don't like to be told what to do all of the time and yelled at. Who does? It wears on a person. He or she feels misunderstood and think their opinion doesn't matter. If yelled at often enough, he or she can take away the wrong idea — that they're a bad person.

I'm not suggesting you allow your kids to make all the decisions and you just go along for the ride. That could be dangerous. Just like there's a reason for a minimum driving age, we as parents certainly need to provide our kids with loving boundaries.

On the flip side of that, we also don't need to be so tight and restrictive with many things as well!

The goal is to find a balance between giving a little, and yet still having healthy boundaries.

Additionally, I will add from my own experience, when children feel understood and listened to, they are more understanding and listen better to us. Seek to understand. The more I do this the more joy and happiness my family and I experience! Keep in mind, understanding doesn't always mean condoning.

How to realign your parenting approach? Read an inspiring parenting book that you resonate with. Find a friend whose parenting techniques you've admired. Set up a time and meet with her, ask her for advice, strategies. Watch her in action! Glean tips from her interactions with her kids. Or, if you want to receive an even more thorough tune-up, do what my husband and I did — schedule time with a family therapist or parenting coach. Remember above all else- listen to your intuition. If what you hear from a therapist or read in a book feels good, follow it. If something feels off, shift gears and find an approach that sits well with you.

SPIRITUALITY

Do you have a regular practice that helps you to feel supported and grounded? Or are you not sure what you believe? Does religion seem hokey to you? Or are you fully aligned with a particular religion or spiritual practice?

For most of my life I didn't have a spiritual practice; nor did I want one. I wasn't sure what I believed; I held both positive and negative thoughts toward religion. I've since reconciled my negative thoughts. I now have a spiritual practice and I have to say, I am much more grounded and happy as a result.

There have been times when the sh@t hit the fan in my house and I quickly stepped outside, connected with Spirit (I went outside and talked to the Universe!) and returned back into the house with a renewed attitude and a stronger ability to handle the situation.

MY SPIRITUAL PRACTICE

Allow me to share how I fuel up for the day so I'm a better mother, and a better person.

I get up each day, head outside (usually regardless of the weather) and exercise, stretch, and talk with Spirit. I work through "schtuff" that's come up during the week. I connect with the feelings I want for the day: Love, confidence and exhilaration. I meditate or write in my journal.

This fills me up with lots of good feelings. I almost always walk away from my time outside connecting with Spirit feeling calmer and happier, I just do.

Not everyone needs to have a practice like mine. This is what works for me. You'll want to find what works for you.

It may be practicing a traditional religion, or meditating, or maybe just spending time in nature. Find what works for you and if you're willing, make it a daily practice, you'll experience more calming, positive results if you do.

MOVEMENT

In RESTORE Key S -Simple Daily Body Cleanse, I shared with you the importance of moving your body to enhance your ability to clean your child's cup (body). Additionally, movement keeps you feeling your best. If you skip exercising for extended periods of time your body feels more sluggish. You may notice a lack of interest in doing much, other then your basic day-to-day activities. You may even become more forgetful and grouchy.

When I've skipped exercising for more than two days, I have felt slower and lazier and it always seems to take me longer to get things done. Not cool.

If you're up for it, help that body of yours move consistently. You'll be a happier mom (or dad) for it!

FINANCES

You don't have to be rich to have balance in the area of finances. You can have balance whether you have a lot of money or not much. If you don't have money, you'll want to sort that out. Seek assistance to get on track. Lack of money can create fear and anxiety, which is never good for your relationship with your spouse or your kids.

Just the act of paying more attention to money, appreciating it when it comes, setting up systems and getting organized with money helps to create more balance. Ignoring money doesn't.

Money needs and deserves your respect. Ask yourself, if money was your best friend how would it say you've been treating it? If money was your best friend, how would you want to treat it? You can use this as a beginning place for cleaning up money and attracting more.

If you already have lots of money, I suggest you still check in regarding your relationship with money- ask yourself the above questions. Your answers will reveal if there's room for creating more balance.

FUN

How much fun do you have? Do you make it a goal to pursue pleasure in your life on a regular basis? Or can you not remember the last time you had a really really great time? Is fun something you squeeze in when you're not busy?

I'll tell you what, pursuing pleasure has not always come naturally for me. I love to have fun, but I've followed that Supermom Mindset of "Gotta get it all done first before fun can be squeezed in." When I finally started to squeeze in more fun, I'd feel guilty I wasn't getting enough done.

It's taken time to create more balance on this one (and continued attention!)

When you try to get a lot done and forget to add fun to your list, you can feel drained, resentful ('cause you're always taking care of everyone else's stuff) and you're no longer being true to you, you're ignoring a very important basic need. That's right; pleasure is a basic need. Without it we wither up. We become mechanical robots without true zest for life.

You *need* pleasure in your life.

It is not an extravagance, but a necessity. Having fun is a way of respecting yourself that fulfills internal needs.

Pleasure doesn't have to come from a big event or big moments. It can come from small moments and everyday actions.

When I give myself enough time to take a long hot shower, that's pleasurable for me. When I get in bed early and read a book, or watch television with my husband while snuggled warmly in bed, that feels terrific!

It's finding everyday activities that you can turn into fun for yourself and it's making time for additional pleasurable activities. If you like dance, take a dance class. If you like reading, join a book club. Schedule in your calendar these extra activities, just as you would commit to a doctor's appointment. Try with all your might to commit to yourself.

If you're up for it, play a game with yourself: try to see how many of your regular daily activities can be turned into fun!

When you let pleasure be your goal, anger and grouchiness dissipate. Love spreads. It can be the beginning of feeling *really* good!

CONTRIBUTION

I've talked a lot about doing less for others and more for you. While doing for you is **hugely** important, I want to be clear, doing for others in a balanced way is important too.

If you help someone out of obligation, you may end up feeling resentful. That's not balanced giving, and ends up serving no one very well.

If you help someone because you really want to, you'll feel good about it in your heart. The goal is to give because you feel moved to. If your heart says yes to whatever volunteer project your contemplating, then that's the green light to give.

Contributing in a balanced way does wonders for your soul. Giving is a beautiful thing — it always gives us, the giver, so much back in return. That's why it can be so difficult for mothers to draw the line with giving. It just feels so good to help!

If you're interested, find a cause to support — school, church, soup kitchen, or whatever speaks to you. Contributing allows you to make a difference in your community, and the world. Contributing also gives you the opportunity to connect with others, to build more positive relationships in your life.

Making a difference and connecting with others is soul food — it will feed your body and life with heaps of uplifting energy.

KEY AREAS OF LIFE- SUMMARY

These key areas of life, when balanced, can have you feeling like a rock star. If you feel like you're far from rock star status, don't fret, you are not alone. I've been there, walked your same walk, have personally worked on creating balance in all of these areas and as my life evolves I continue onward with this balancing journey. Just the awareness and act of trying is all you need sometimes for things to feel better.

The reason I suggest creating balance in these key life areas is because once you do, everything changes. You see things differently — what once felt like a major problem with your kids is now something you know you'll figure out how to handle, when the time is right. You begin to think differently, noticing how cool your kids really are. This was always there in front of you, it was just hard to see when you didn't feel so good and were caught up with so many other life concerns. You begin to feel more open and confident with yourself, you see and feel life as a good thing, not just work.

Moving toward more balance in these life areas will light up your life and your children's! When it comes to finding just the right answers and helping them in ways you once thought impossible, you are now open to possibilities! You have the energy, and with that, beautiful changes for your children are inevitable!

WRAP UP!

As I sat down and realized how I created the foundation for healing my sons, I uncovered these **7 RESTORE Keys** and the **HELP Heal Mindset.** I've shared quite a bit, so in the event you're scratching your head trying to remember all the information, here's a little overview:

HELP HEAL MINDSET

H- Honor Your Feelings
E- Everything Happens for a Reason
L- Learn From Your Children
P- Prioritize YOU

7 RESTORE KEYS

R- Reality Rewritten

E- Eat All Natural Real Food

S- Simple Daily Body Cleanse

T- Thrive in Natural Balanced Environments

O- Om, Listen to Your Intuition

R- Respect and Appreciate Yourself

E- Establish Balance in Key Areas of Life

Before this book, my actions were just the actions of a mother looking to find the best means possible to bring healing to her sons. I searched, tried new things, and tried some more. Having walked this walk for some time, I feel comfortable in saying if you can find it in yourself to practice living the 7 RESTORE Keys and work on acquiring the HELP Heal Mindset, you open up to the possibility of restoring your child to the beautiful potential that was always there. It just needed some support to really shine!

In the end, you must do what feels best for you.

My heart goes out to you on this journey. If this approach resonates with you- go for it! I look forward to looking around and seeing more healthy vibrant children filling our world!

Sending you gratitude, for the time you are taking to read this!

DON'T DO THIS ALONE

If you choose to follow the same healing route I did, go slow. One step at a time is all you need to make a BIG difference.

If along the way, you have difficulty sticking with it (because I sure did) keep in mind it's normal to get stuck, feel overwhelmed or just want to give up. This is when it's valuable to have go-to people to support you. Have certain friends who know what you're up to, who you can call in a pinch, friends that can talk you out of that rabbit hole!

Please, please, don't go this alone. Remember that's the Supermom Mindset and that sets you up for reaching plateaus, not getting as far as you need and want. Being a post-Supermom myself, I tried to go this alone for a long time. Nope, it didn't work. That's how I burnt myself out and started to feel terrible. When I reached out and worked with my first coach, I felt a huge sense of relief. Someone who could finally help me to see where I was stuck. Someone who had my best interest in mind and was there showing me what to do. Someone who helped to ignite sparks in me that led me to where I am today — healed children, and wonderfully happy!

If you're ready to LIVE the 7 RESTORE Keys and acquire the HELP Heal Mindset so that your entire family benefits, I'd be happy to talk with you. If the idea of working together appeals to you, then let's connect. I'd be honored to support you on your healing journey with your kids.

CONTINUE TO INVEST IN YOUR FAMILY'S WELL-BEING

If you've decided you want further support to apply what you've learned here to real life, so you and your family can experience a greater level of healing, visit www.IHealedMySons.com.

You decide what feels best. You can start small and sign up to receive free ongoing how-to tips, advice, and support to continue to clear your child of their ASD and help them thrive. That may be enough for you at this point.

If you feel you're ready for even greater results that come with working more intimately with someone, I invite you to schedule yourself for a Strategy Session.

You can reach me through my website: www.IHealedMySons.com or send me a quick email: Andrea@IHealedMySons.com.

THANK YOU TO MY FAMILY

What you read here was a good portion of what I did to help create a beautiful level of healing for my sons. It's been an amazing journey, one of the most difficult I've ever faced and yet it's been the most amazing, beautiful journey ever! I wouldn't change it for the world. Honestly.

My sons have opened my eyes to what is most important. They've helped to clear me of the gunk thoughts I previously believed, all those thoughts that held me back. My sons have helped me to become healthier, physically and emotionally. My sons have opened me up to love more. They've also led me to being confident, to caring more for them, for me, for others.

I love you Forrest and Boden, how blessed I am to have you in my life, showing me the way. Thank you from the deepest most loved filled places in my heart. Thank you.

This thank you wouldn't be complete without appreciating my husband for being with me every step of the way. Some of our steps were shaky- (okay, many of them were!) But, we somehow continued to step together. Shane, you inspired me in small ways when you didn't even know it. You taught me through everything I begrudged about what you were doing — those were your teachings and your gifts to me. Just like our sons, you've helped me to grow. We've grown stronger together for all that we've been through. I love you, Shane. I couldn't have done this without you. Thank you from the deepest places in my heart.

MORE GRATITUDE

I feel so blessed to be connected with so many strong, guiding souls. Some of you were guiding me when you didn't even know you were. I watched you in action and learned by example.

I want to thank my entire family: **Mom** and **John**: I love and appreciate your kindness, true caring and continuous support. Through your example you've taught me to be generous with *my* love. And mom, you have so deeply demonstrated what it means to be Strong and Courageous. Thank you.

Dad and **Dee**: You've respected and supported me going against the grain- being me, being different- I learned some of that from you Dad! Thank you for your ongoing love, and life lessons, I carry them with me in my heart.

My sisters **Stacey** and **Dee**: You are both strong women who inspire me with your authenticity and ability to speak up for yourselves. I love that you are my sisters.

My in-laws, **Susan** and **John**: Thanks for caring so deeply, loving us through thick and thin! Our relationship has helped me to grow more compassionate. Thank you.

The **Aiken family**- I love you! You've championed me to do this, to write this book. Your love of our family and me has helped me to be stronger and move through obstacles that I could have let hold me back. Thank you- from my heart.

Thanks to the friends I've connected with who have helped me to believe in myself and this book.

Lisa Alexander: You helped me to better realize it was time to do it, get out there and make a difference. You my beautiful friend were the first to plant a seed to pay attention to vaccinations. You introduced this idea before I was ready. But, lucky for me I came around. Thank you for your foresight. Thank you for all the years of love, it's a beautiful thing that we've stayed connected for so long!

Mimi Stevens: You sensed I was capable of greater things. Thank you. I love that we are still lovingly connected. You've inspired me through the years and have touched my heart with your friendship and generosity. I will love you forever!

Cathy Whelehan: Your words of wisdom always helped me to align myself with the Truth.

Charlotte Siddiqui: Your strength and openness has always intrigued and inspired me.

Carrie Reilly, Laura McDonald, MaryBeth Thomas, and **all the Waldorf teachers** we've connected with: Your wisdom, kind spirit and ability to see a better way to nurture and support my sons has always sent goose bumps down my spine. You are awesome!

Jodi Knuff: You've got it goin' on girlfriend, I watch as you gently, yet firmly support your family and I'm always in awe, thank you for your example!

Pam Davis: You knew all along I could do it. Thanks for cheering me on and empowering me when I would get sidetracked.

Joanne Keane: You are awesome! You're real. You represent LOVE. You are an amazing example of living kindness and compassion. Your love has allowed me to further heal and live in a more empowered way. I deeply appreciate your support and value our friendship. You inspire me to be my best! Thank you.

Alex Jamieson: You inspired me to write my first book- I never did publish it, but going through that process, having you hold me accountable helped me to see I could do it. It was completely possible. I smile when I remember us driving in the car rattling off chapter titles. You ROCK! Thank you for your guidance and touching my soul with your bright shinning spirit.

COACHES

Karin Witzig Rozell and **Drew Rozell:** You are literally a dynamic duo! I've connected with you several times over the years, during which you've positively influenced the course of my life. Most recently you've supported me in creating this book. With your guidance I've been able to more clearly share what's in my heart.

Joshua Rosenthal: YOU showed me there was more. You helped me to see my soul for the first time; it was in that glimmer that I was hooked. I'm deeply honored to have learned from you. Thank you. My soul thanks your soul.

Supriya Denissov: You shined a bright light on my inner greatness, so I could see it better, your wisdom and guidance stays with me to this day, I love you.

Rose Payne: You spotted years ago (and suggested to me) what I just recently have come to understand: appreciate, appreciate, appreciate. Thank you for your clarity and guidance.

Kristen Domingue: In one session you saw with laser clarity what my purpose is. Others had said this may be my purpose, but you went beyond spotting it, you helped me to see and feel for myself that this was the case. Never before did I have this clarity. Thank you for opening up a new life for me.

COACHES FROM AFAR

I feel it's important to extend gratitude to the coaches I admire and respect and have followed from afar. Through your books and video tips I've gained clarity and momentum, have learned, grown, and have been genuinely inspired to live a rock star purposeful life. I love you all and feel enormous gratitude for the love you're spreading in the world. Thank you for sharing your gifts!

Jenna la Flamme: I started watching your videos to glean marketing technique ideas through your dynamite example and ended up following your deeper guidance to add more pleasure to my life. Thank you for this.

Michael Ellsberg: You and Jenna are an inspiration! I love your relationship, and love the fountain of wealth your book represents. Your book has reminded me that my past "failures" were important and that my perseverance to be an entrepreneur that makes great money making a major difference in the world is not only possible but my Truth. Thanks for keeping my inner light glowing!

Marie Forleo: You just ROCK!!! Not only do I LOVE your dancing but, it was one of your blog posts urging, "Just friggin do it" that got me off my butt and had me start writing this book. Thank you, I feel enormous gratitude for the love and greatness you spread.

DOCTORS

Dr Eileen Comia: You started us down this path of holistic living. Wow, I feel enormous gratitude for the clearing you helped us accomplish early on in my sons' lives. Your initial guidance and knowledge opened the doors to a world of my sons living FREE of autism. Thank you for shinning a light in what could have been dark times. How blessed we are. Thank you Dr Comia!

Dr Joshua Berry: Your spirit lives on through my sons and in our hearts. You were my sons' first naturopath. Your love and support brought us to even higher levels of healing- you will always hold a special place in our hearts- always.

Dr Kathleen Riley: You are an amazing woman- I honestly think you were a shaman in another lifetime. You combine science and intellect with powerful intuition. Thank you for supporting my family and keeping us healthy with only what serves us best. I know, whenever we hit bumps in the road, you are there providing just the right remedy to help create balance once again. Love and gratitude to you Dr. Riley.

Dr Cushing: You are a kind generous man with amazing knowledge. Your holistic techniques have made life easier for my sons (and I). Because of you foods that were once taboo can now be consumed comfortably and life feels easier and lighter as a result. Thank you for your beautiful support.

For all family, friends and additional experts we've worked with that I didn't mention by name, you are in my heart and I sincerely appreciate you and the love you add to my life. It's really all this love that's made this book possible. Thank you.

ABOUT THE AUTHOR

Andrea Anderson is an author, speaker and powerful coach to mothers who have a child with ADHD, autism or any ASD.

Andrea is dedicated to showing women around the world how to create the same level of beautiful healing that she's achieved with her own sons.

Andrea facilitates live and tele-seminars.

With her down-to-earth, playful-yet-powerful style, Andrea conveys ideas and information in ways that create aha! moments and inspire women to go after the impossible!

Andrea combines eight years of personal hands on-in-the-thick-of-things experience of healing her sons of ASDs with a bachelor's in Psychology from Southern Connecticut State University and a dual certification in

Health Coaching from the Institute for Integrative Nutrition in New York and Columbia University Teachers College.

Andrea lives in Connecticut with her supportive husband Shane, two amazing sons, Forrest and Boden, and two loving cats.

For fun Andrea loves to DANCE-anywhere, anytime — at parties, in her living room, in the car. If there's music, she'll move her booty!

Additionally, Andrea loves spending time outdoors, yoga, swimming and relaxing at the beach, hiking and playing with her family.

To schedule keynote presentations, seminars or retreats, or private coaching with Andrea visit: www.IHealedMySons.com